"Travel is a part of the human experience, and it should not come at the cost of our planet. *Sustainability in the Air* serves as a map, showing us the routes we can take to reduce our carbon footprint in the sky."

—**Aradhana Khowala,** board member of World Tourism Forum, Chair of the Global Advisory Board at Red Sea Global

"*Sustainability in the Air* is a reality check for the industry, capturing both the challenges of earning green credentials and the hopes of a resilient industry driven by innovative opportunities."

—**Jeffrey Goh**, CEO of GulfAir and former CEO of Star Alliance

"As a percentage of global emissions, airlines will continue, and likely increase, their current contributions whilst new technology is being developed. However, do not despair; in *Sustainability in the Air*, Shashank and Dirk provide a practical guide on bridging that gap over the next decades."

—**Alex Cruz**, Vice Chairman of WestJet, ex-CEO of British Airways

"Innovators in aviation are responsible for leading the change towards sustainable practices. This book showcases the pioneers making it a reality."

—**Luis Felipe de Oliveira**, Director General of ACI World

"We're all on the same team when it comes to our planet, and *Sustainability in the Air* offers insights into a greener future by showcasing the innovations transforming aviation for the better."

—**Mark Pilling**, veteran aviation journalist

"Much like the rise of Silicon Valley revolutionised technology, *Sustainability in the Air* reveals how a new generation is transforming the aviation industry for the better, ushering in an era of sustainability."

—**Mario Hardy**, envoy at the Sustainability Global Tourism Center

"Exploring the future of air travel, *Sustainability in the Air* provides profound insights into the industry's adaptive journey towards catering to an increasingly eco-conscious global population."

—**Dr. Joe Leader**, CEO of the Airline Passenger Experience Association (APEX)

"*Sustainability in the Air* is an inspiring call to action for individuals, industry leaders and policymakers to embrace change and work toward a more sustainable and responsible aviation sector."

—**Gregg Saretsky**, former CEO of WestJet, Corporate Director of IndiGo Airlines

SUSTAINABILITY IN THE AIR

INNOVATORS TRANSFORMING AVIATION
FOR A GREENER FUTURE

SHASHANK NIGAM & DIRK SINGER

SimpliFlying

ISBN: 978-1-956955-80-4 (ebook)

ISBN: 978-1-956955-81-1 (paperback)

Dedicated to:
Parineeti & Sanskriti,
Ben & Charlie.

May this book serve as a pledge to protect
the skies you will one day explore.
May the magic of flying live on.

ABOUT THE AUTHORS

Shashank Nigam is the founder and CEO of SimpliFlying. Having consulted for more than 100 airlines over 15 years, Nigam is a frequent keynote speaker and has been widely featured in major media outlets like *The New York Times, The Wall Street Journal* and the BBC. His previous book, *SOAR,* was an Amazon bestseller and is currently being taught to Masters  students at Cranfield University (UK) and Embry-Riddle (USA). *Sustainability in the Air* is his second book, and he is the host of a leading podcast with the same name.

 Dirk Singer is the Head of Sustainability at SimpliFlying, an industry-leading aviation consulting firm dedicated to shaping a greener and more environmentally conscious future for air travel. He is also the co-founder of several successful creative agencies including Honey, Rabbit and Cow. Singer's career has spanned more than two decades, during which he has written white papers, newsletters and essays on climate change related issues, reaching thousands of subscribers in the aviation industry. *Sustainability in the Air* is his first book.

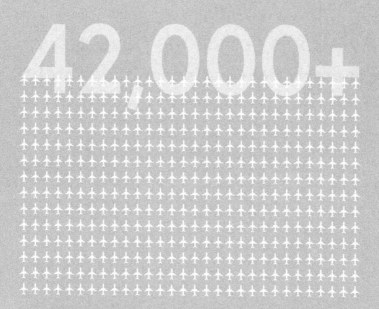

By 2042, the global aircraft fleet will be ~50% larger, **growing from 29,000 to 42,000.**

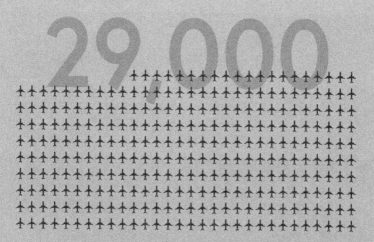

Source: "World Fleet Report 2023", Avalon, "Commercial Market Outlook 2023-2042", Boeing, June 17, 2023, https://www.boeing.com/commercial/market/commercial-market-outlook

2023 2024 2025 2026 2027 2028 2029 2030 2031 2032 2033 2034 2035 2036 2037 2038 2039 2040 2041 2042 2043 2044 2045

Aviation's emissions have grown dramatically and disproportionately.

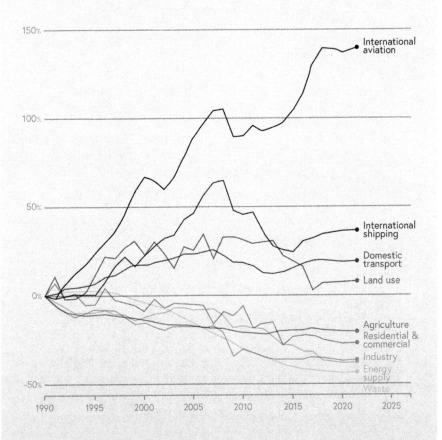

If nothing is done, **aviation's share of global emissions** could rise from **2 to 22%** by 2050.

Only 1% of the global population is responsible for
half of aviation's emissions.

Source: Stefan Gössling & Andreas Humpe, "The global scale, distribution and growth of aviation: Implications for climate change", *Global Environmental Change*, Volume 65, November 2020, https://doi.org/10.1016/j.gloenvcha.2020.102194

Airlines are expected
to cut emissions.
Today.

77% of respondents across 30 countries believe airlines have the **responsibility to address climate change.**

| 77% | | 17% |

Source: Bailey, Pippa, "Earth Day 2022 – Global attitudes to climate change", *Ipsos Global Advisor*, April 18, 2022, https://www.ipsos.com/en-us/news-polls/global-advisor-earth-day-2022

EIGHT
NET ZERO ACTIONS

Tie growth to Sustainability
Decouple any growth from emissions

Combine the carrot and stick
Use mandates and incentives in tandem

Emphasise cooperation
Net zero is too big a task for anyone to achieve on their own. The industry needs to work together

Apply the polluter pays principle
Introduce fair carbon pricing along with a clean skies fund raised from ticket sales

Aim for true zero
Aim for a true zero future in the long-term, where aviation has next to no climate impact

Focus on global equity
Spread the benefits of aviation decarbonisation around the world, not just the Global North

Transparency and targets
Build trust through transparency, and have targets audited by credible third parties

Take only a fair share
When developing SAF and new technologies, take only a fair share of finite resources

CONTENTS

PREFACE

WHY THIS BOOK AND WHY NOW?

In 1935, Imperial Airways took 12 days to fly from London to Australia with multiple stops enroute. Today, that journey can be done non-stop in just over 17 hours. That means the benefits of mobility are now within reach for more people than ever, who thanks to air travel can do everything from take up new employment or study opportunities to visit friends and family to broaden their horizons by experiencing different cultures.

Of course, today, aviation faces a new challenge: decarbonisation and sustainability.

This book is all about how aviation, one of the hardest-to-decarbonise industries, can make that transition and become more sustainable. But why do we care?

To put it simply: because flying is magical. It is a social, cultural and economic good. It's one of the most remarkable human endeavours. It's made the world a smaller place.

And because both of us, your authors, are products of aviation.

Dirk was born in Tokyo and grew up in places as diverse as the US, Jerusalem and Edinburgh. Shashank was born in Delhi, grew up in Singapore and has lived everywhere from Kampala to Whistler to Doha. We have worked for most of our careers with over 100 airlines. We know the magic of flying. At the same time, we also understand the dilemma aviation faces in balancing growth with sustainability, given the industry's increasing contribution to global warming.

Aviation's sustainability flight path must be led from within by the insiders (the airlines and manufacturers) and innovated by and with the outsiders (the technology firms). In writing this book, we have conducted over 300 hours of interviews with top aviation and technology executives working on decarbonising the industry. Most of these stories are being shared in print for the first time.

This book starts with a few critical charts and an introduction that defines the importance of why airlines cannot go about business as usual. The first half of the book then dives into how the outsiders—technology entrepreneurs with little or no aviation background—are creating radical solutions toward sustainability, from electric and hydrogen aircraft to eVTOLs. The second half of the book showcases how industry insiders like manufacturers and airlines are transforming their organisations amidst these challenges, taking action for a sustainable future. Finally, we conclude with a call to action for the industry, travellers and those with influence.

It is our deepest desire to preserve the magic of flying for future generations. That can only be done through immediate and strong action on multiple fronts. We hope this book inspires future generations to work with airlines on a sustainable path or build companies that can catalyse this journey. The time to act is now.

Shashank & Dirk
London, UK

PART ONE
INTRODUCTION

WELCOME TO THE SILICON SKIES

IN 2017, Executive Director of the Steve Jobs Archive Leslie Berlin[1] talked to veteran tech journalist Kara Swisher about her book *Troublemakers: How a Generation of Silicon Valley Upstarts Invented the Future,*[2] which charts the rise of Silicon Valley from 1969-1983.[3]

"The whole thing reminds me of the Beatles," Berlin said. "In 1963, they're doing Little Richard covers, and by 1970, they've completely transformed music and the broader culture."

The computing revolution brought changes quickly that the world didn't see coming. "The video game industry was born, the personal computer industry was born, biotech," Berlin said.

Hearing Berlin explain it, it's easy to understand how exciting that initial wave of innovation, invention and creation of a whole new set of industries and technologies must've been.

Fortunately, we are arriving at a similar kind of moment right now; this time, it is happening in the climate space, among a new generation developing technologies that will help different industries wean themselves off fossil fuels and meet their net-zero goals. And one of those is aviation.

Since it came into existence, aviation as a sector has been

3

almost totally dependent on fossil-fuel powered aircraft. Today, there are literally hundreds of start-ups looking at how to change that, and how to make flying much less carbon intensive in the process.

The founders of these companies, a few of whom we profile in this book, want future generations to benefit from all the social, economic and cultural benefits of air travel, but to do so without feeling that they are doing excess damage to the planet.

This mission is part of what makes the collision of aviation sustainability and climate tech so exciting: it combines a wider social good with huge economic potential.

If you're wondering how huge, Boston Consulting Group Chairman Rich Lesser has described Climate Tech as a trillion dollar opportunity.[4] On Bloomberg's *Zero Podcast*, venture capitalist Dipender Saluja went further, talking about it as "the biggest opportunity in the history of the world."

One veteran Climate Tech investor even expects to see the creation of at least 500 unicorns—companies valued at $1 billion or more—in the sustainable tech sector.[5] In a conversation with Bloomberg, Sean O'Sullivan, founder of venture capital firm SOSV said that "there is no way this is not happening", given that "major industries will be reinvented."

The reason investors are so bullish about the long-term opportunity is simple: to decarbonise fossil fuel dependent industries is a very long process involving a lot of complexity and coordination. There are many steps in the process, and each one is its own world of opportunity and possibility.

WE CAN DECARBONISE EVERY PART OF THE JOURNEY

In aviation, here are just some of the different steps to consider in that long journey:

- **Ground Handling**: Airlines contract ground handling companies to help with everything from check-in to baggage loading and unloading. The largest of those companies, Swissport, has already set a minimum of 50% of electrification of its ground vehicle fleet by 2025.[6] Airports themselves are moving towards using renewable energy, with some even building their own solar farms, such as the Airport Solar City project in Edmonton, Canada.[7]

- **Taxiing**: Aircraft burn fuel while keeping their engines running at airports. Amsterdam's Schiphol Airport has been testing the deployment of so-called TaxiBots, two semi-robotic taxiing vehicles that carry out pushbacks and tow aircraft. Schiphol says that this way of taxiing can significantly reduce fuel consumption and therefore CO_2, nitrogen, and ultrafine particle emissions.[8]

- **Fuel for Flight**: Obviously, planes need fuel to fly. Hydrogen and electric powered aircraft are being developed, but will initially be used for smaller regional aircraft on shorter flights. Until this technology scales up, non fossil-fuel alternative fuels, known as Sustainable Aviation Fuel (SAF), will be needed. The feedstocks to make that fuel will need to be developed, and you then need both production facilities, and refineries. One estimate says that up to 7000 refineries will be required globally to handle these new alternative fuels by 2050.[9]

- **Eco-Friendly Design**: There's scope to do everything from reduce the seat weight, saving fuel, to eliminating single use plastics, with plastic being itself a petroleum-based product. Meanwhile, there are modifications to designs of aircraft, such as including winglets, which reduce fuel consumption, along with new carbon fibre materials being used, which extend range and reduce fuel burn.

- **Next-Gen Aircraft**: Hydrogen and electric power are proven fossil fuel alternatives—but someone needs to design, certify and produce aircraft that can use them.

These examples barely scratch the surface of the innovation and invention that needs to take place in *aviation*—though of course, any inventions or technologies developed that benefit aviation also almost always benefit other industries as well.

This is good news, because if you broaden our view to the *many other* carbon intensive industries, like shipping or construction, that also need to be decarbonised, the scope of work to be done and the opportunity it represents start becoming clearer.

WE'RE NOT EVEN SCRATCHING THE SURFACE OF WHAT'S NEEDED

It's small wonder that more than a quarter of all venture capital investment went into climate tech in 2022, according to PwC,[10] but even then, European VC firm World Fund estimates only 16% of climate finance needs are currently being met.[11]

World Fund says that based on current climate targets, that funding needs to increase by at least 590% annually to $4.35 trillion. In other words, for however much activity there has already been in the space, there's soon to be exponentially more activity —and also that investors who act early can stand to reap significant financial benefits.

World Fund's white paper quotes PwC research where 60% of institutional investors report that ESG (Environmental and Social Governance) investments resulted in higher yields in their investment performance compared to non-ESG equivalents. In fact, according to a peer-reviewed study from Oxford University, global decarbonisation and weaning the world off fossil fuels could save the world at least $12 trillion.[12]

It means that a world without fossil fuels results in solutions that are not only cleaner and better; they're also cheaper.

In 2020, former *USA Today* editor David Callaway wrote an article headlined "Zeus: The Coming Battle with the Climate Gods."[13]

Callaway's article referenced Zeus as both the prime god in the Greek pantheon and also the god of weather, but as he explains in the article, there is no deity coming to save us from extreme weather and global warming in the next few decades.

Instead, it will be other people: "ambitious group of innovators, entrepreneurs, eccentrics...divining new strategies, concepts and projects to help us adapt."

NEW OPPORTUNITIES AND A COMPLETELY NEW SECTOR

Though the sections mentioned before are greatly distilled, our hope is that they hint at the scale of the challenge humanity has ahead, as well as the challenges the aviation industry is soon to face specifically—and all of this should set the scene for what follows in this book.

Whether our readers are executives, founders, engineers, investors or simply interested citizens, our hope is that this book will help paint a picture of years to come.

We will begin by outlining why aviation's decarbonisation challenge is so hard to overcome before discussing some companies who are focused on doing so, among them well-established companies and brand new startups producing synthetic fuels which are potentially almost net-zero and others designing completely new kinds of aircraft.

In every case and story, there are many lessons to be learned for interested parties of all kinds, and the most crucial takeaways from each are summarised at the end of each chapter for convenience (particularly for anyone studying the field for insights they might apply elsewhere).

The good news is that given what we've learned through research and writing, we're optimistic that the 2050 net-zero goal can be met—and when it is, we're also confident that the companies and individuals profiled in this book will have done a lot of the work to make that happen.

AVIATION'S EXISTENTIAL PROBLEM

ON MARCH 1, 2023, a Lufthansa flight from Austin, Texas to Frankfurt Germany hit a patch of turbulence—and not the common, mild shaking that passengers tend to remedy by tightening their seatbelts and waiting patiently for a few minutes for it all to be over.

On this occasion, the aircraft had to be diverted to Washington DC's Dulles Airport after seven people were injured from various objects thrown around the cabin during the turbulence.

"It was kind of in slow motion," passenger Susan Zimmerman later told ABC News. "Like in a movie where you see everything lift and then all of a sudden it comes right back down. It was shocking."[1]

According to Dr. Paul Williams, a professor of atmospheric science at Reading University in the United Kingdom with expert knowledge of aerial turbulence, it is clear why incidents like the one Zimmerman described are becoming increasingly common.

"We've been warning for the past decade that climate change would increase turbulence," Dr. Williams said, "and now we see it happening."[2]

A report co-authored by Dr. Williams and two fellow academics pointed to an increase in a phenomenon called "clear air turbulence," which "is hazardous to aircraft and is projected to intensify in response to future climate change."[3]

More commonly understood, climate change is leading to a general worsening of the atmospheric qualities necessary to create a smooth flight experience for passengers. It is all happening as a result of burning larger and larger amounts of fossil fuels, which in turn leads to greater and greater emissions of greenhouse gases.

The accumulation of all the above is that CO_2 levels in our atmosphere are the highest they have been in three million years[4]—and unfortunately, the aviation industry has contributed to that accumulation.

A difficult fact is when we fly, we're burning a lot of carbon; arguably even more difficult to face is the fact that as individuals, flying is one of the most carbon-intensive things we can do. To illustrate just how intensive, German non-profit Atmosfair claims that by flying from London to New York, our carbon footprint in that moment becomes higher than the *annual* average for people in 56 countries.[5]

While aviation is a significant contributor to global greenhouse emissions, at 2-3%, the industry's share is still lower than industries like iron and steel or livestock and nature, at 7.2% and 5.8%, respectively.[6] But aviation's percentage is increasing as more and more people fly.

In 2001, the aviation industry flew 1.7 billion passengers. By 2019, the year before the COVID-19 pandemic, that number had grown to over four billion.[7] Those numbers are now set to grow even further. In Europe alone, Eurocontrol, the EU body for managing air traffic, projects the number of flights to increase by 44% by 2050.[8]

Other areas of the world such as Asia-Pacific will see even faster growth. Airline trade body IATA says that the Asia Pacific region is expected to add around 2.5 billion additional passenger journeys compared with the 2019 level by 2040. The result will be an almost doubling of worldwide air traffic between 2019 and 2040, from roughly four billion in 2019 to eight billion passengers a year in 2040.[9]

With other industries such as the automotive and power sectors making progress on decarbonisation, air transport, on its current trajectory, could be responsible for 22% of all global greenhouse gas emissions by 2050.[10]

Then there is the issue of aviation's *non*-CO2 effects such as nitric oxides, sulphur dioxide and water vapours, the latter being responsible for the formation of contrails, the visible cloud-type trails formed behind aircraft.

According to an IPCC Report, contrails could account for 35% of the aviation industry's global warming impact.[11] (Contrails, and how airlines might avoid forming them, is something we consider in more detail in Chapter 2 on Etihad.)

None of this has escaped the attention of climate activists and environmentalists, who are increasingly turning their attention to air travel with a few common questions: Why do we need to fly so much? Is the industry doing enough to decarbonise?

THE ELEPHANT IN THE ROOM: FLIGHT SHAMING

Had you been in Nantes, France in September 2022, you might have spotted an unusual looking ad at the local bus stop. At first glance, it would've had the look and feel of an airline advertisement: the ad featured an aircraft with the logo of Dutch airline KLM on it. A closer look would've revealed the aircraft to be circling above a burning planet.

Coinciding with bus stop ads in France were roadside ads in Rome, Italy, this time featuring the logo of ITA Airways, an Italian airline, though changed to read "ITA Failways." Beside the logo was a picture of a pterodactyl and a stark slogan: "We are flying towards the next extinction." In London's Shoreditch district there were similar ads, including a billboard with Lufthansa's logo and a man looking out a plane window at a forest fire below.

A hashtag Lufthansa has been using in their marketing is #SayYesToTheWorld. On the billboard in Shoreditch, it had been changed to #SayYesToTheEndOfTheWorld.[12]

The above are just a few examples of guerrilla advertisements that ran in 15 European cities,[13] all coordinated by guerrilla marketing groups Subvertisers International[14] and Brandalism.[15]

Both groups had ambitious common goals for their campaign, namely an end to all fossil fuel ads in Europe including airline advertisements, with the argument that airlines were doing a lot of talking about phasing out fossil fuels while actually doing very little.[16]

According to Tona Merriman from Brandalism, the group's choice of subverting advertising poster sites was deliberate. "The allure and glamour of high-carbon lifestyles such as frequent flying has been purposefully crafted by the advertising industry," Merriman said, "and shows no signs of relenting—despite [Summer 2022 being] one of the hottest summers on record."

Taken together, all of these phenomena send a clear message: the evidence is out there, and the public is taking notice.

WHERE CULTURE LEADS, REGULATORS FOLLOW

In IPSOS-MORI's 2022 Earth Day Report,[17] 77% of respondents in 30 countries agreed that airlines had a responsibility to address their contributions to climate change by reducing their carbon emissions. In 2021, another study from the same organisation found that across 29 countries, 14% of respondents had even started flying less for business or leisure because of climate change concerns.[18]

In response, industry leaders have started to raise the alarm about what these changes in popular perception will mean for aviation if the industry doesn't take actions to decarbonise. In a February 2023 interview, Marco Troncone, CEO of Aeroporti di Roma (Rome Airports), warned that a business-as-usual approach would be "very dangerous in terms of negative restrictions and punitive policies."[19]

"Chances are high that in five years' time, the level of attention [on polluting industries] will be higher than [it is] now," Troncone said. "And at that time, there will be zero tolerance. If there is tolerance, it will only be given in exchange for a promise [to cut emissions], which must be credible."

His point was also made earlier that year at a January 2023 webinar hosted by Deep Tech Showcase, when Gregory Davis, CEO of electric aircraft manufacturer Eviation, spelt out some of the logic behind these shifts quite clearly. "Where culture leads," he said, "regulators follow."[20]

In other words: as goes public opinion, so go government authorities.

Changes are already taking place in countries like Norway and Denmark, as both countries now have deadlines in place for domestic flights to be fossil-fuel free by 2040 and 2030, respectively.[21] [22]

Meanwhile, the Netherlands has been trying to cap the number of flights at Amsterdam's Schiphol Airport,[23] while Belgian authorities have introduced new taxes on shorter flights and private jets.[24]

France has even banned a small number of flights that could otherwise be accomplished by a train journey of two and a half hours or less,[25] while raising air travel taxes to invest more in its railways.[26]

Similar discussions about flight caps and encouraging citizens to use alternate transport are happening in countries all over the world, and they show no sign of stopping.

AVIATION'S $4 TRILLION GOAL OF GETTING TO NET ZERO BY 2050

The organisation in charge of regulating global aviation standards is the International Civil Aviation Organisation (ICAO), a specialised agency of the UN. As such, regulations and announcements from the ICAO are made, in effect, on behalf of the UN's membership of 193 different countries—and in October 2022, the organisation agreed to set the global and long-term aspirational goal of achieving net-zero emissions by 2050.[27]

In response, Dan Rutherford and Shraeya Mithal of environmental think tank The International Council on Clean Transportation (ICCT) called the agreement "noteworthy," appreciating that the organisation was turning away "from merely offsetting emissions and toward measures to dramatically reduce CO2 [emissions] from planes and fuels."

Expanding their comments, the authors said the ICAO's announcement:

> ...envisions deep cuts in aviation CO2 to near-zero levels by 2050, which ICAO estimates will cost up to $4 trillion US, and it invites member states to regulate aviation emissions themselves rather than relying on ICAO to develop minimum global standards covering all countries.[28]

But even if there is relative consensus among interested aviation organisations and various governments, how might that $4 trillion net-zero decarbonisation goal be realised?

As the ICCT's aviation and maritime programme director, Rutherford is well-versed in how challenging these shifts will be for the aviation industry—though as it turns out, the ICCT, which is a technical observer with the ICAO, has produced a blueprint for how certain ambitious goals for 2050 might be accomplished.[29]

"We felt it was useful to have an independent, transparent roadmap to complement what industry and governments have put out," Rutherford said. "It's a combination of 'how low can we conceivably go by 2050,' and then back casting it to what's needed."

The "how low can we go" approach is illustrated in a scenario that the ICCT has named Breakthrough. Here, "early and sustained government intervention triggers widespread investments in zero-carbon aircraft and fuels, peaking fossil jet fuel use in 2025 and zeroing it out by 2050."[30]

"[We would] throw as much as we can at the problem in terms of sustainable aviation fuel, operational improvements, new aircraft and pretty aggressive carbon pricing," Rutherford said, "[getting] us down to more than 90% reductions in 2050 relative to 2019 levels and cutting cumulative emissions by a little more than half." As he puts it in simpler terms: "It's sort of our 'kitchen sink' scenario."

THE ROLE AND IMPACT OF CARBON PRICING IN REACHING NET-ZERO GOALS

As Rutherford illustrates, the Breakthrough scenario is the most aggressive one the ICCT has projected. Even so, it still allows aviation to use many different measures in order to reduce its carbon footprint, even if not all the strategies used are equally aggressive.

One of those strategies is carbon pricing, wherein emissions can remain nearly the same for certain parts of the industry provided that the companies responsible have the funds available to "buy" them.

The best known example of this kind of carbon pricing plan is the European Union's Emissions Trading System (EU ETS), which sets a limit on the total amount of greenhouse gases that can be emitted by certain sectors of the economy. Accordingly, airlines are required to surrender allowances for every tonne of CO2 they emit.

Currently, the ETS applies to inter-European flights, but the

EU is assessing whether to extend it to flights departing from Europe to non-European destinations. In addition, any free allowances currently applied to airlines are scheduled to be phased out.

Another complication of carbon pricing schemes like ETS, as with other market-dependent reduction strategies, is that their effects may simply rebound onto consumers—that the result of these regulations could mean that passengers will have to pay a lot more for flights.

In a *Financial Times* article on new EU emission rules, Olivier Jankovec, director-general of airports industry body ACI Europe, warned that these approaches would see "increasing costs for airlines, increasing fares and lower demand." For his part, Michael O'Leary, the CEO of Irish low-cost carrier Ryanair, commented that the "era of absurdly cheap fares was over."[31]

AIRLINE INITIATIVES TO ACHIEVE NET ZERO BY 2050

Of course, airlines are not simply standing still while regulators suggest action. Instead, they are swapping out their older gas-guzzling aircraft for newer and more fuel-efficient models. The Airbus A321neo, for example, is a narrow-body plane which Airbus claims will deliver fuel improvements of up to 20% per seat compared to similar aircraft.[32]

In addition to fleet renewal programmes and higher carbon pricing, airports are also making operational improvements, including new air traffic control measures to optimise flight paths and group in-flight aircraft together more closely, thereby reducing delays and average flight times while improving fuel efficiency.

Of the strategies mentioned, carbon pricing, transitioning to more fuel-efficient aircraft, and streamlining operations can all be done immediately.

Meanwhile, research and development of new types of aircraft that don't run on kerosene—either through battery-electric or hydrogen powered propulsion systems—are also currently underway. Even though they will initially be used on smaller planes and shorter routes, these aircraft are true-zero, not net-zero, as they don't burn carbon.

Some industry leading companies working on this technology are profiled throughout this book, though the earliest these kinds of aircraft are projected to start flying is 2025. Still, while the ICCT does include future Zero Emissions Planes (ZEPs) in its Breakthrough scenario model, the single biggest element of it is allocated to Sustainable Aviation Fuels (SAFs).

SAFs are alternative fuels not made from fossil fuels. While in most cases SAFs are not completely carbon neutral, they still offer a typical CO_2 life cycle reduction of up to 80%, with a few newer types even claiming reductions of 95%+.

IS SUSTAINABLE AVIATION FUEL (SAF) A SILVER BULLET?

At the 2023 Arabian Travel Market (ATM) in Dubai, Brian Moran, Boeing's Vice President of Sustainability, pointed out that as of May that year, there were 23,000 commercial aircraft in the skies—a number that could easily increase to 40,000+ in the next two decades.[33]

Since aircraft like the Boeing 737 or Airbus A321 have a typical lifespan of 30 years or more, many of the planes flying today will still be flying in 2050. In order to decarbonise aviation, then, developing alternative fuels that will be compatible with these existing aircraft is crucial.

"That's what makes SAF so promising," says Robin Hayes, CEO of US airline JetBlue. "It works with existing infrastructure and aircraft technologies. Aeroplanes delivered today can continue to fly in the future with an increasing share of SAF as it becomes more available in the market."

While aircraft are still only certified to fly with a 50% blend of SAF, the other 50% being conventional fuel, Hayes says that, "we expect that we could be operating flights with 100% SAF around 2030."

This is why Boeing's sustainability strategy, according to Moran, depends on what the company calls "SAF and." Practically speaking, it means that even while Boeing is researching next generation aircraft, the company is simultaneously making an even bigger bet on SAFs.

SAF comes from a number of different "feedstocks," including used cooking oil, agricultural waste, forestry waste, and fuel crops like acanthus or jatropha. A new breed of SAFs known as Power to Liquid (PtL) fuels are e-fuels made from renewable energy sources like solar, wind, and hydroelectric power.

E-fuels are typically produced by combining hydrogen with carbon dioxide captured from either the atmosphere or other industrial processes—and because they have a higher energy density than biofuels made from crops and don't use land that could be used to grow food, they are becoming increasingly favoured by policymakers.

For reasons outlined by Moran, new mandates are being introduced requiring airlines to increase the proportion of SAF used in their overall fuel mixes. In ReFuelEU Aviation's April 2023 mandate, for example, the EU announced that flights departing from EU airports will need to be 2%, 6%, and eventually 70% SAF-based by 2025, 2030, and 2050, respectively.[34] In addition, the EU also wants an increasing share of those e-fuels to be made from renewable energy, with a 2% mandate for 2032-2035.[35]

In the United States, the Biden administration has likewise put a heavy emphasis on SAFs. In 2021, it committed the US to producing three billion gallons of SAF and reducing aviation emissions by 20% by 2030.[36] Even so, there are three reasons why SAFs haven't already been deployed more widely.

First, they are expensive, with cost estimates ranging from two[37] to eight times[38] more than conventional jet fuel (with e-fuels at the upper end of the range); second, there simply isn't enough of supply; and third, producing SAF is very resource intensive.

For the US government to achieve its goal of producing three billion gallons of SAF for domestic use, the country would need to increase its production by 122% year on year.[39] Given all this, it may come as no surprise that as recently as 2019, SAF only accounted for 0.1% of all jet fuel used worldwide.[40]

IS AVIATION ASKING FOR MORE THAN ITS FAIR SHARE?

Activist group Stay Grounded calls air travel "the most unequal mode of transport," claiming that 80% of the world's population has never set foot in an aircraft and that a small minority of frequent flyers—1% of the world's population—accounts for 50% of aviation emissions.[41]

Since aviation is only one of a number of industries in need of renewable energy, biofuels, and hydrogen, and given that most people around the world don't fly, all of this begs the question: is aviation asking for more than its fair share of finite resources?

A paper published in Science of the Total Environment, an academic journal, examined the issue in more detail, noting the "implications of preferential access to land and clean energy for Sustainable Aviation Fuels."[42]

Authored by Dr. Susanne Becken and Professor Brendan Mackey from Griffith University, Australia, along with Professor David S. Lee from Manchester Metropolitan University in the UK, the paper concluded that decarbonising the aviation industry via SAF could mean using 9% of global renewable electricity for e-fuels and 30% of sustainably available biomass for biofuels by 2050.

According to Dr. Becken, the danger is that if aviation "[grabs] all the clean energy so that aviation is net-zero by 2050, there will be nothing left for anyone else, [delivering] an overall worse outcome than had [it] just given it to the electricity sector." To illustrate, she offers the example of wood chips produced by the forestry industry, with forestry waste being a feedstock that can be used to make SAF:

> *Say we've got one coal-fired power plant. They want the wood chips for the boilers, so we don't use coal. We've got the dairy industry—they have a lot of boilers, they are still coal boilers. They say, "We want wood chips." Then we've got an airline that says, "We want the wood chips to turn them into SAF." It's completely clear that the airline case is weaker, because it delivers so little carbon reduction. I've calculated that it's one tenth [of the impact we would make] if we gave it to the hungry power plant instead.*

Dr. Becken's research has led her to think seriously about the future of aviation. "I like flying," she said, "and I wish the answers were different, but when you start to contrast some of the other needs and some of the other CO2 reduction potential, I'm afraid that after having crunched the numbers for twelve months now, aviation just doesn't look good."

E-fuels, a newer and more promising kind of SAF, don't need feedstocks like wood chips or used cooking oil or a fuel crop like acanthus, but they do require renewable energy. In December 2022, European Venture Capital firm World Fund came out with a knowledge paper claiming that replacing even 8% of Europe's aviation fuel with e-fuels by 2040 would require the equivalent annual electricity consumption of the Netherlands or Sweden.[43]

It's why in an interview on the *Land & Climate* podcast, climate activist Finlay Asher wondered aloud whether the airline industry shouldn't just be allowed to burn fossil fuel-based kerosene, calling e-fuel powered flights "probably the most inefficient thing you could do [because of the renewable energy needed to make e-fuels, barring] putting [e-fuel] into a rocket and sending Jeff Bezos into outer space."[44]

As a former aircraft engineer and co-founder of Safe Landing,[45] an organisation that campaigns for "industry leaders to conform with climate science," Asher believes burning jet fuel and using low-carbon energy for other uses would be the better approach if the aviation industry were growth capped.

"Burn less and less every year," he said, "and slowly your electric and your hydrogen and some alternative fuels in limited quantities will start replacing those. That's kind of the conclusion that I end up at."

Dr. Becken agrees with Asher's assessment. "In some ways, It would make much more sense to let aviation have the kerosene and decarbonise everything else to get the biggest bang for the buck," she said—though like Asher, Dr. Becken believes the change would need to be combined with curbs on aviation growth and a potential reduction in yearly flights.

CAN FREQUENT FLYERS FINANCE DECARBONISATION?

With ICAO estimating the price tag for aviation decarbonisation at $4 trillion dollars, the ICCT issued a report showing how they could raise 81% of that figure with a global frequent flyer levy.[46] If implemented, those who increase their carbon emissions by flying more often would pay more, which is a proposal Dr. Becken said she would, in principle, support.

"People will laugh that you can fly for the price of a pizza, or that the taxi [to the airport] costs more than the flight, and that's just not right," she said. "I think that's where we need to say, 'Okay, that obviously has just gotten a bit mad.'"

Under the ICCT's proposals, the first flight travellers might take each year would be free, allowing people to go on vacation or visit relatives during holidays without paying a surcharge. After that, fliers will pay a levy on a sliding scale on a range from $9 for the second flight to $177 for their 20th.

Though these changes may have an effect on demand for flights, the ICCT's aim with their report wasn't to stop people from flying. "We wanted to reframe the debate of frequent flying away from demand management and towards revenue generation," Rutherford said. "We focused on the $4 trillion figure, broke that down into a per ticket cost and then modelled out a hypothetical levy schedule."

Upon looking at all the data and putting together a model, Rutherford said that a couple things stood out.

"A frequent flyer levy could be surprisingly effective as a means of addressing what we call the 'differentiation challenge,'" he said. "Anytime you have a global policy, you need to make sure it represents common but differentiated responsibilities. It's a UN term which in essence means making sure richer countries that have more capacity to pay the bill, move first and move harder. And we found that actually, the frequent flyer levy was very effective for that."

As a result, people in developing countries flying for the first time won't face a charge. Instead, the bulk of the levy will be paid for by people who can afford to fly multiple times every year—though that would still represent a small minority of people in very high income brackets.

Rutherford also said that the distribution of the levy matches historical carbon emissions. "We can't just look at emissions today," he said. "We have to consider the emissions that have occurred over the past 40, 50, or 100 years when we're laying out the burden of regulation."

"What we found in that report," he continued, "is that a frequent levy actually works very well so that the share of revenue generated by country matches closely with each country's contribution to historical aviation emissions."

Through these combined advantages, Rutherford believes an international frequent flyer levy could raise revenue for sustainability changes in an equitable way. Of course, since such a scheme would have to be implemented globally, there are a number of questions about how it could be done.

One solution, according to Rutherford, would be to do it

through industry wide bodies such as the International Air Transport Association (IATA), the trade association of the world's airlines.

"Obviously, IATA is reluctant to embrace the frequent flyer levy, as the airlines are so dependent on revenue from the frequent flyers," Rutherford said. "But IATA already does things like act as an international clearinghouse for payments across itineraries. And the airlines, as we know, collect a lot of data about their customers' propensity to fly."

Though Rutherford conceded that industry opposition will make it unlikely such a plan might be adopted in the next few years, it could be possible in the medium-term.

What might change minds in the future is a reduced public tolerance for industries perceived to be polluters. As such, aviation will need to continue to embrace more radical measures to keep the public's trust.

A RAY OF HOPE: LESSONS FROM THE SOLAR INDUSTRY

While the ICCT's frequent flyer levy proposal could pay for much of decarbonisation equitably, it still doesn't address Dr. Becken's concern about the enormous resources needed to make enough SAF to sustain the industry. It also doesn't solve the issue that alternative technologies such as hydrogen or battery-electric power are still very much in their infancy.

With time running out for the aviation industry to meet its net-zero target, rapid innovation and progress are needed to answer all of these questions about cost, scale, resources, and technological development.

Here, the solar power industry provides a model of what's possible, as solar has recently changed from being the most expensive to the cheapest power source within several decades.

When US President Jimmy Carter had 32 solar panels placed on the White House East Wing in June 1979, it was seen as an eccentric thing to do.[47] At the time, solar energy wasn't perceived as an answer to America's energy needs, particularly because the energy from the panels cost a whopping $36 per watt.[48] Perhaps not surprisingly, the much more fossil-fuel friendly Reagan administration that followed ended up taking the panels down.

But many years have passed since then, and the situation has changed. As of 2020, the International Energy Agency (IEA) said that solar, at less than $0.20 per watt, was the "cheapest electricity in history"—even cheaper than fossil fuels in most countries.[49]

Of course, there are multiple reasons solar became a cheap power source. First, the technology improved, and solar panels became more efficient and less expensive to manufacture. After that, economies of scale ensured that as demand for solar panels increased, this also decreased the cost of production. Finally, governments implemented policies to support the development of solar energy through tax breaks and subsidies.

Taken altogether, these policies helped make solar energy more affordable for consumers and businesses.

ELECTRIC FLIGHT TO THE RESCUE

A similar trajectory to the solar industry may be possible in sustainable aviation, particularly as it pertains to batteries.

Sceptics of electric aircraft point out that batteries are not energy efficient enough to power flights for anything but the shortest of distances, and as a result of battery weight, even those flights will only be able to carry a few passengers at a time.

As of 2023, only one electric aircraft was widely used and certified: the tiny Pipistrel Velis Electro,[50] which can fly one pilot and one passenger for less than an hour.

Though the larger nine-seat Eviation Alice flew a successful test flight in September 2022, the company's CEO Greg Davis has admitted that the battery that would allow the aircraft to fly its intended 250 nautical mile range doesn't yet exist.[51] But all of that may be about to change as a result of battery innovation.

"We've seen steady improvement of around 3-7% per year in energy density," said Nathan Milliecam, President and CEO of Utah-based battery company EP Power Systems,[52] "[but] we are starting to push some of the boundaries of what traditional lithium ion chemistries can do." According to Milliecam, those little jumps have more recently turned into 20-30% improvements year on year.

"I don't know if it's realistic to think you'll see that 20-30% improvement every year," he said, "but as you start to move to different chemistry families, you'll see those curves continue. So we're very optimistic about the future." On the strength of these advances, a number of battery manufacturers have announced new batteries with much-improved performances.

In a May 2023 interview on the *Allplane* podcast,[53] Richard Wang, CEO of advanced lithium metal battery developer Cuberg, part of Sweden's Northvolt Group, said his company was developing an aviation-suitable battery with an energy density of 400+ wh/kg.

Chinese manufacturer CATL claimed to have gone even further by building a battery with an energy density of 500 wh/kg; for perspective, the batteries in today's Teslas deliver around 265-280 wh/kg.

At the Auto Shanghai trade event in April 2023, CATL claimed their new battery would accelerate the "electrification of sea, land, and air transportation; open up more possibilities of the development of the industry; and promote the achieving of the global carbon neutrality goals at an earlier date."[54]

That 500 wh/kg barrier was also broken by California-based Amprius, which in March 2023 announced a battery that uses Silicon anodes in lithium-ion batteries, rather than the graphite that's commonly been used until now.[55] Amprius believes that the use of silicon will substantially improve the performance of electric vehicles, aircraft, drones, and wearables.

While EP Power Systems has tested a 400 wh/kg battery,[56] Milliecam says that energy density isn't the only metric you need to look at. "Cycle life is ultimately what closes the business case," he said. "If [a battery] only lasts 50 or 100 cycles, you're retrofitting your aeroplane every other week."

Similarly, charging times can also be a concern. "I have a Tesla and I can drive it all day long and I can charge it all night long and it's just fine," Milliecam said. "That fits my use case perfectly. But in aviation, we discharge the whole battery or a significant portion of the battery every time we fly the aircraft. And aircraft only make money when they're flying, so turn-around time is very, very important."

As Millecam points out, airlines will likely need to be able to charge an aircraft and turn it around in 20 minutes. "[If not], then it's really difficult for operators to make money," he said. "We have that technology. We have the fastest charging cell in the world. But most importantly, we don't degrade our cycle life as a result of that fast-charging mission."

All these advances in battery technology are pushing the idea of what's possible with all-electric aircraft even further, which Millecam says is one of the most exciting things about the field.

One Colorado-based startup called Cosmic Aerospace is already looking into producing a 25-seat, battery-powered plane that could fly for 1000 km[57]—all with the help of batteries being developed by companies like CATL, Amprius, Cuberg, and EP Power Systems.

MAKING GREEN HYDROGEN CHEAP AND ABUNDANT

In addition to electric flight, the aviation industry is placing a significant bet on hydrogen-powered aircraft as a major zero-emissions solution. Supporters of hydrogen highlight its superior energy density compared to batteries, which could enable longer flights beyond short regional routes. Companies like Airbus are exploring the use of liquid hydrogen as an engine fuel, with the goal of having a hydrogen-powered plane in the skies by 2035.[58]

Other players, such as ZeroAvia[59] and Universal Hydrogen,[60] are adopting hydrogen-electric or hydrogen fuel cell propulsion systems. These systems store hydrogen in tanks which is then pumped into a fuel cell to generate electricity, powering an electric motor on the aircraft.

However, critics have raised concerns about the limited availability and high cost of green hydrogen, which is produced from renewable energy sources by separating water ($H2O$) into hydrogen ($H2$) and oxygen ($O2$) via electrolysers.

They point to the fact that green hydrogen production is energy-intensive because the electrolysers used in the process are expensive. While greenhouse gas intensive "grey hydrogen" costs around €1-€2 per kilo, as of 2023, green hydrogen can cost as much as €8 per kilo.[61] As a result, 95% of hydrogen production is accomplished using fossil fuels .[62]

Nevertheless, innovators are actively working to address these challenges by developing more affordable and efficient electrolysers. Singapore startup SungreenH2, for instance, claims its electrolysers offer a 50% cost reduction and 75% improved energy efficiency compared to standard models.[63] In Australia, Hysata secured over $29 million in an oversubscribed Series A funding round to establish a pilot factory aimed at producing the "world's cheapest green hydrogen."[64]

This gives Universal Hydrogen CEO Paul Eremenko grounds for optimism. He envisions a future where the cost of green hydrogen will be on par with jet fuel without subsidies by the mid-2020s. In addition to the advances in electrolyser technology, Eremenko points to what he calls "the massive subsidy" provided by the US Inflation Reduction Act, amounting to $3 per kilo of green hydrogen.

Acknowledging there will be a latency period before the subsidies kick in, and that new hydrogen projects will require both demand and favourable economics, Eremenko still predicts an impending capacity surge in the coming years, likening it to an "avalanche of hydrogen."

WHY WAS 80% OF SAF FROM CALIFORNIA IN 2023?

Advances are also coming in SAF production from businesses like Air Company,[65] which has found a new way to make fuel from captured CO2 and hydrogen.

Air Company's new process is more than twice as energy efficient as the conventional method to make e-fuels (called the Fischer-Tropsch method), and is starting to provide answers to some of the hard questions about using renewable energy to produce e-fuels.

At the same time, SAF producers are benefiting from an increasingly helpful global regulatory environment, particularly in the United States. The 2021 US Sustainable Skies Act and the 2022 Inflation Reduction Act, for example, provide SAF producers with credits of $1.25 per gallon so long as they reduce greenhouse gas emissions by at least 50%.[66] This has been complemented by state-level SAF incentives, including the Washington State Senate Bill 5447 establishing a per-gallon incentive for SAF of up to $2 per gallon.[67]

In California, the combination of statewide programmes such as the Low Carbon Fuel Standard (LCFS) and federal incentives are resulting in local producers receiving benefits of up to $3.60 per gallon.[68] Because of all this, California was responsible for producing 80% of the world's supply of SAF as recently as 2021.[69]

This remarkable achievement has caught the attention of Marjan Rintel, the CEO of Dutch airline KLM, who is urging the European Union to adopt similar subsidy programmes to those implemented in the United States so that there is "a real incentive in place for the production of SAF at reasonable prices."

However, Rintel emphasises that the responsibility does not solely lie with governments. She sees a significant role for the corporate sector in driving the adoption of SAF. Major corporations, which often spend millions of dollars annually on employee travel, can contribute to the development of alternative fuels by purchasing SAF for their flights.

Rintel believes that this signal must come from the CEOs of these corporations, as "CEOs have an objective to reach a certain level of sustainability," unlike purchasing departments primarily focused on cost considerations.

This belief that the corporate travel market can help drive SAF adoption and build economies of scale is shared by JetBlue CEO Robin Hayes. "With proper investment and policy incentives, there is opportunity for the SAF market to grow and benefit from the economies of scale needed to bring SAF closer to parity with traditional Jet-A," he says. "What remains for a cost premium could very well be met with the support of corporate partners through purchase of SAF certificates or book and claim initiatives."

Book and claim is an approach where a company purchases a specified quantity of SAF for their flights. The actual fuel, however, is mixed into the industry's fuel chain and can be used anywhere. This system is akin to households on a renewable energy tariff purchasing an equivalent amount of renewable energy to power their homes while still receiving electricity through the grid.

A notable example of a book and claim product for businesses is Avelia, a blockchain-powered system developed by American Express Global Business Travel (Amex GBT) and Shell Aviation. This solution facilitates the procurement of SAF, enabling companies to actively contribute to the growth and utilisation of sustainable fuels in aviation.[70]

When it comes to incentivising SAF production, Haldane Dodd, director general of Geneva-based Air Transport Action Group (ATAG), which represents the commercial aviation sector, feels that the UN body ICAO may have a role to play.

"ICAO can add a government role to this process to help to

underpin that long-term thinking," Dodd said. "Importantly for us, it does a couple of things. First of all, it says to governments, 'Hey, you're on the hook as well. You need to also put in place the right policies to help support SAF deployment around the world'—but also for the finance industry, the energy industry. They are going to really need to step up in ways that they haven't so far."

As Dodd emphasises, in order to motivate governments to adopt these changes, there needs to be balance between stick versus carrot approaches. "Whenever we talk about mandates with governments, we say, 'Actually, that's a useful backstop to any kind of policy that you can put in place to help support the supply of SAF.' Because there's no point in just having the demand there from a mandate if you don't have the supply there actually to fulfil that mandate."

When considering the total capital expenditure needed for global SAF production, Dodd sees a difficult but possible challenge ahead. "The cost we think might be required is around $1.5 trillion over the next 30 years. That's about $48 billion a year on average or around 6% or 7% of the typical oil and gas capital expenditure that is usually spent. So actually, it's not out of the realm of possibility. But that's where financing comes in."

BIG OIL NEEDS TO WEAN OFF THE "BLACK STICKY STUFF"

In addition to governments, Dodd feels that oil giants need to step up more as well; even though some are already engaged, as a whole, the industry still seems fixated on the old ways of doing things.

"The demand for alternatives to fossil fuels is going to grow over time," Dodd said. "If I was looking at the future of my company or my industry, if I was an oil person, I'd be looking to say, 'Hey, we're going to have reduced demand from the consumer market—from cars, trucks, and aviation as well. I might as well start getting into this opportunity very early on.'"

"Some of them have started to take up that challenge," he continued. "Others haven't. You'd have to ask them why they can't seem to pull themselves away from oil, but I'd imagine it's because it's incredibly profitable."

As Dodd explains, the profits made by the five of the largest oil companies in the world were $200 billion in just one year—though it appears to be coming at a great cost.[71]

"They can't continue to operate that way," he said. "It's not going to last forever. Maybe they're just grabbing whatever they can while they can while it still lasts, but if we're going to tackle the climate crisis, we're not going to be able to keep pumping fossil fuel out of the ground."

Jenny Kavanagh, Chief Strategy Officer at hydrogen-powered aircraft company Cranfield Aerospace Solutions, says the giant profits made by Big Oil are both a source of hope and worry. "It would be nice to say what gives me the most hope is something inspirational, but it's not," she said. "What gives me most hope is the almost unlimited greed of humanity. It's like when we found oil: 'What's that black sticky stuff coming out of the ground?' And people were all over it."

"That's my hope," she continued. "When people start to realise just how much money they can make out of this and that the old black sticky stuff is hiding to nothing, it will happen. The question is, will it happen quick enough? That, to me, is the crux of the problem. And we knew how bad it was 30 or 40 years ago and did nothing."

If nothing changes, the outcome, according to Kavanagh, is bleak—which is what makes her so passionate about weaning aviation off of fossil fuels. "I actually saw a schematic showing strips of temperature of the globe," she said. "It went back from 1901 and then projected up to 2100, which shows that some of the Northern Hemisphere would basically be uninhabitable."

Despite Kavanagh's assessments, Dodd is optimistic that aviation's net-zero goals can be achieved—particularly because so much of the research, planning and groundwork has already been done to show the aviation industry exactly how.

"We did a whole heap of work to figure out what is possible given our growth profile, given the technology that we know is available, given things like feedstocks for sustainable aviation fuel," he said. "Yes, it's an enormous challenge. But it is doable."

PART TWO
LOOKING FROM THE OUTSIDE IN

ONE
HEART AEROSPACE: HOW A HUSBAND-AND-WIFE TEAM PIONEERED ELECTRIC AIRCRAFT IN SWEDEN BY REIMAGINING REGIONAL AVIATION

ON HIS WAY to the Swedish Parliament to talk about electric aviation in early 2018, Anders Forslund has a memory that stands out.

"There was this high school student protesting about climate change outside," Anders says. The girl's determination left an impression on him. "I thought it was pretty cool. But at the time, it was the sort of thing that didn't go any further than the local news."

That student was Greta Thunberg—and throughout 2018 and 2019, her influence started to spread far beyond Sweden. As we all now know, her passion inspired a wave of similar youth-led climate protests around the world.

Out of simple local activism, Thunberg had captured the popular imagination—so much so that by the end of 2019, she had become Time's Person of the Year.[1]

One of the causes that Thunberg took up was that of "fly-gskam", better known by its English translation of flight shaming.[2] This is the idea that because aviation is environmentally harmful, it is also socially irresponsible for consumers to fly.

Thunberg herself famously refuses to fly, having even gone

so far as taking a catamaran across the Atlantic for her 2019 North America tour.[3]

Anders has a very different idea about air travel, calling it "one of the most genius inventions in history." His conviction is why when Thunberg was in a catamaran in the middle of the ocean, he and his wife Klara were hunched in front of their computers in a large hangar in Gothenburg, Sweden.

To transform the entire aviation industry for the better, they were building a company to develop a completely new and environmentally sustainable aircraft—one that would emit no carbon dioxide, have a minimal noise footprint and be cheaper to operate than fossil fuel-based planes.

As respective CEO and CBO (Chief Business Officer) of Heart Aerospace, Anders and Klara put four years' work into developing their new aircraft the ES-30, a hybrid-electric powered plane unveiled at the company's bi-annual Hangar Day[4] on September 15, 2022. This is Heart's event, where they showcase progress and milestones to the media, partners and investors.

With a radical approach of their own, Anders and Klara are taking their own steps toward a sustainable future with the ES-30—a future that, unlike Thunberg's, still includes the marvels of modern aviation. "The ES-30 is designed to transform regional air travel," Anders said, "with input from airlines around the world."

Of course, before we celebrate, all of this begs several questions:

Even if the technology is incredible, how can regional (in other words, short-range) aircraft ever solve the international (and thus long-range) problem of the climate crisis? And with more than 100 other companies focused on regional and hybrid-electric aircraft, what sets Heart Aerospace apart in such a crowded field? [5]

Apart from an impressive list of airline backers and investors, the reason for Heart's traction and momentum may be attributable to the Forslunds' wide-range vision—one that's easiest to illustrate by starting at the beginning, before their company existed.

THE ROMANTIC ORIGINS OF HEART AEROSPACE AND THE "SUGAR WATER MOMENT"

For as long as he can remember, Anders has loved to play the guitar in his spare time to relax and clear his mind.

"Music is actually about simplicity," he says. "It's not about how many chords you know. It's about what you choose to do with the things you know." As he explains, his sense of romantic idealism has been in his DNA forever—and before Heart Aerospace even existed, he brought it with him into aviation.

In 2016, Anders was studying for a PhD in aerospace structural design at Chalmers University of Technology in Gothenburg, and part of the program included going to MIT on a scholarship through a research exchange. While he was there, Anders became interested in drones, and sometime later, Elon Musk came to talk about the potential of electric planes.

"I became really fascinated by the fact that there was new technology that was so simple, so cheap, and so easily commoditised," Anders says. "It opens up the design space."

Anders had been researching the connections between the growth of aviation as an industry and its effects on climate change as part of his PhD programme. As he learned, the flight path that aviation was on wasn't very sustainable; still, Inspired by all the new technology he was encountering, ideas were starting to form in Anders' head.

"Looking at graphs of aviation emissions going to 2050, I knew that a lot of work was going into the incremental optimisation of the different components of aircraft engines to result in one percent improvements here and there," Anders says. "Yet aviation was growing on average by five percent every year."

If those industry trends continued, the climate implications would be significant—but change wasn't coming fast enough.

Compounding the problem were technological and logistical limitations and the industry's reliance on fossil fuels. But after his exposure to electric aircraft and advances in drone flight, Anders could see a different possible future.

Considering all this, Anders had a problem: he didn't want to join the ranks of the aerospace incrementalists, even though that was the path he seemed to be on.

The question before Anders was simple. As he puts it himself: "Am I going to follow the trajectory of the people that came before me? Or am I going to try and set a different path so I can do something meaningful?"

Anders had what we call a sugar water moment. This refers to a now-infamous story about Apple's co-founder Steve Jobs.

In 1983, Jobs started searching for a new CEO at Apple, particularly someone with marketing acumen.

He approached John Sculley, the then-CEO of Pepsi-Cola, who had recently overseen the "Pepsi Challenge" marketing campaign that resulted in the company outselling Coca-Cola.

Though Sculley seemed perfect for the job, it was, in some ways, a tough sell; Pepsi-Cola was an established giant and Sculley was in a role that reliably promised him money, security and corporate esteem.

Apple, meanwhile, was still relatively small, high-risk and unproven, even if the product and the future they were selling was intriguing.

To persuade Sculley to join him at Apple, Jobs pitched to him in the form of a question: "Do you want to sell sugar water for the rest of your life or come with me and change the world?"[6]

Similarly, Anders didn't want to spend the rest of his life working on aircraft engines that for decades had largely stayed the same. He wanted his work to mean something.

Instead, he wanted to help create a better future, and he decided to do it by going all-in on electric aircraft.

All he needed was a commercial opportunity to make it

happen, one that came in 2018 when Norway announced that all of their domestic flights would have to be electric by 2040.

In a moment, everything clicked. Someone would have to *make* the electric planes connecting all the remote communities in Norway; why couldn't it be him? That same year, Anders and his then-fiancée Klara founded Heart Aerospace, with Anders serving as CEO and Klara as Chief Strategy Officer.

Now, all they needed was to develop their product: a revolutionary, regional hybrid-electric aircraft.

LAST-MINUTE CREATIVE FUNDRAISING STRATEGIES—OR, HOW TO RAISE $2.2 MILLION WITH LETTERS OF INTEREST (LOIS)

Already, a portion of Heart Aerospace's expansive vision was beginning to take shape.

As the world continued to come to grips with climate change and began taking action to mitigate it, governments would begin rolling out new regulations and laws to incentivise the development of more sustainable technologies.

The aviation industry was no exception, though what kinds of technology would be incentivised and for what uses would vary from place to place.

In Norway, the first incentives were aimed at domestic flights. The opportunity was beginning to look regional.

As such, Heart Aerospace's initial plan was to develop and build a 19-seat regional aircraft, called the ES-19, that would be powered by electric batteries alone. Certification would be easier for a smaller plane, Anders and Klara reasoned, and a 19-seater was the right size for short, regional hops.

Anders did the first designs himself using nothing more than CAD software, with the aim of having the ES-19 plane in commercial service with airlines by 2026.

Even so, the idea and opportunity on their own weren't enough. Building a new aircraft would be highly capital intensive, and Anders and Klara would need that cash upfront to even get started. Unfortunately, the reality was few airlines were willing to commit cash upfront for an as-yet-unproven concept.

Today, Sweden has electric car companies like Polestar, but in 2018, that eco-system largely didn't exist.

In spite of those difficulties, Anders and Klara kept researching how they might fund an electric aircraft in Sweden when they learned about Y Combinator, the American start-up accelerator headquartered in Mountain View, California that helped kickstart over 3000 companies including Airbnb, Door-Dash, Dropbox, Quora, Stripe, and Twitch.

They had also helped Boom, a supersonic aircraft company, which featured prominently in the media due to its ambition of reintroducing supersonic flight after Concorde stopped flying in 2003.

Anders and Klara applied alongside 12,000 other applicants. Though getting accepted into Y Combinator still wouldn't guarantee their success, they knew it would raise the profile of Heart Aerospace, connect them to an exclusive and valuable network of entrepreneurs and tech investors and teach them strategies on how to run a start-up.

Finally, they got word from Y Combinator: Heart Aerospace was one of just 200 that got through.

With their first milestone behind them, Anders and Klara moved from Sweden to Mountain View, California. The next big one came on March 18th, 2019, when they were invited to participate in Y Combinator's Demo Day.

On Demo Day, founders were given the chance to get on Y Combinator's stage to pitch the merits of their company in front of 400 established VCs and other potential investors.

It was the opportunity that Heart Aerospace needed so badly, namely a direct line to an ocean of risk capital and an audience who was primed to understand the potential of their vision.

Even so, however idealistic the entrepreneurial ecosystem around Y Combinator may be, the investors' underlying goal was still to make money; as such, it would still be a tough sell.

"How do you convince big investors when you only get two minutes on stage?" Anders asks. "How can you convince them to put money into a two-person company taking on Airbus and Boeing?" With Demo Day closing in, neither Anders nor Klara had a clear strategy, and both thought their pitch was underwhelming.

"We didn't have anything in terms of technology," Anders said. "How could we show traction? How could we show that we were the people who could do this?" Under pressure and with time running out, Anders and Klara had an idea.

"We'd heard that when Boom Supersonic had been in Y Combinator a few years prior, it had gotten Richard Branson to sign a Letter of Interest," Anders said.

Boom successfully secured investments on Demo Day, likely boosted by showing up with an LOI in hand.

For a company like Heart Aerospace that didn't have much to show investors in terms of a proven product, securing an LOI from an aircraft company was an enticing strategy that would certainly help its chances.

On the other hand, since Heart's business plan was to begin in Norway, Heart's potential corporate customers were halfway around the world, and Anders and Klara were in California.

Securing an LOI would require building a relationship and earning the trust of various Scandinavian aviation companies, all of which would involve expensive flights overseas for in-person meetings with no guarantee that any of it would pan out. Even so, neither Anders nor Klara had a better idea.

As ever in stressful times, Anders' creative side kicked in. With some familiar Bob Dylan lyrics in his mind about having nothing and thus having nothing to lose, [7] Anders and Klara decided to return to Sweden to see if they could secure expressions of interest from airlines, even though Demo Day was only weeks away.

"We flew back to Stockholm and to Oslo and approached the airlines SAS, Wideroe and Braathens," Anders said, "and we ended up actually getting all three of them to write an LOI."

When Demo Day arrived, Heart Aerospace was more than just an idea. Along with a 3D-printed model plane they mounted on a camera tripod, they had not one but three signed letters of interest from airlines, and potential customers, in their pocket. Putting it all together resulted in a killer pitch, which Anders paraphrases as follows:

You may not be aware of this, but Norway wants all its flights to be electric by 2040, and a similar trend is happening in Sweden. This is a billion-dollar market—and we know this, because we have LOIs from three Scandinavian airlines. Ultimately, electric planes will fly all over the world and there will be a market worth billions of dollars.

The audience was impressed, which included representatives from EQT Ventures, a big Swedish venture fund who agreed to be lead investors in Heart Aerospace's first round.[8]

Anders and Klara's plan had succeeded: they were leaving Demo Day with an investment. When they closed their seed round in May two months later, they had successfully raised $2.2 million in seed money—enough money to grow a team that could make their vision a reality.

WHY AEROSPACE STARTUP ENGINEERS AREN'T (AND CAN'T BE) LIKE *SILICON VALLEY* CODERS

When the average person hears the word "start-up," the image that likely comes to mind is something out of the HBO comedy *Silicon Valley*,[9] namely a bunch of coders fresh out of college living together in a messy, shared house with empty takeaway pizza boxes everywhere.

As Anders explains, aerospace start-ups are nothing like that. While there are plenty of internet-based businesses that began as apps hacked together by college-aged coders and later became unicorns, before an aviation company can legally transport people through the air for hundreds of miles or more, they first need to jump many hoops and meet exceptionally rigorous safety standards.

After that, there is plenty of additional complexity involved in everything from developing the cockpit software to designing engines.

Unlike many other tech businesses, aviation companies need to keep all of these factors when it comes to recruiting talent.

While enthusiasm is great, the common "move fast and break things" culture of certain start-ups has to be avoided. Because of this, hiring a team with an institutional background in aviation is often very important.

Even so, just as Steve Jobs was able to hire John Sculley away from Pepsi-Cola, Heart Aerospace hasn't had a problem attracting top talent from larger companies—and Nigel Pippard, one of Heart's first hires and current Executive Technical Advisor, is just one example.

Originally from the UK, Pippard became a naturalised US citizen through his stints at various American aviation companies.

After spells at helicopter maker Leonardo and British Aerospace, Pippard held a position at Saab as chief engineer in their avionics division before Heart Aerospace reached out. "I had a director-level role," he said. "I had a nice salary with a decent pension. As the saying goes, I had my 'feet under the table.'"

Then one day he got a LinkedIn message from an old colleague.

Nigel says that "there was a picture of the Heart ES-19. And a question that said something like, would you give up your job at Saab to work on this?"

He knew that electric aviation was risky and largely unproven. But it was also potentially world changing. "And so I replied, instantly, yes."

Nigel's fist meeting was with Anders and Klara at an

industry event. The second started in their Gothenburg apartment.

"Then, they drove me out to this facility that they had just signed a lease on. And here was this grand purpose made facility with hangars and offices. It was a former corporate flight operation centre for Volvo and Ericsson. And it was just beautiful. But there were just the three of us, and we're walking around, and it was kind of surreal."

After a few meetings, what finally swung Pippard into leaving Saab was Anders's vision. "You really have to get to know Anders, right?" Pippard said. "When you listen to him and hear his rationalisation and explanation for everything, you realise this is a guy that has actually got it figured out. He is just an exceptional human being on many levels."

Pippard isn't the only person to comment on the uncanny first impression caused by Heart Aerospace's facilities.

While raising capital, Anders later approached Lowercarbon Ventures, a climate tech fund headed by legendary tech VC Chris Sacca—who ranked second on the Forbes Midas List of top tech investors[10] and was once a former judge on the TV show *Shark Tank*—to see if they wanted to invest.

Lowercarbon Ventures did agree to invest, and in a later interview shared on Stanford University's eCorner in February 2022,[11] Sacca said his only regret was not investing more—but he also described the encounter in a story that has since become part of Heart Aerospace's mythos.

"A guy named Anders from Sweden showed up," Sacca said, which prompted the Lowercarbon team to ask, "where are the rest of you?" Anders' response? "Don't worry, I've got this."

After hearing Anders' pitch and consulting with Airbus and Boeing about his idea for a 19-seat electric aircraft (they were sceptical), Lowercarbon ignored the doubters and invested. Sacca's only regret now is that he didn't put in even more money.

So now, "he's got this huge hangar," said Sacca.

"But for the first year and a half, he just sat in the corner of the hangar and started hiring some computer scientists and aerospace engineers who designed the plane using machine learning and AI!"

As strange as it sounds, Anders confirms the story is very true. "It was this massive hangar that had been built only a few years previously but had not been used," he said. "It was like a private jet hangar. We were like, "We'll take it!' They thought we were crazy."

That decision turned out to be strategically sound. As Sacca detailed in his Stanford interview, Heart Aerospace went on to build a full-scale powertrain and reduced scale fuselage at a fraction of the usual cost by doing it on computers, all with a team small enough to fit inside one of the 19-seat aircraft they were building.

"It shows how the tiniest team can build something massive by leveraging computers," Sacca said. The purchase seemed doubly wise as time went on and the Heart Aerospace team had room to grow; today, it has ballooned to more than 160 people.

Another crucial hire for Heart was Claudio Camelier, the company's head of marketing, product strategy and market analysis, and the process was similar to Pippard.

In all, Camelier had spent more than 20 years at aerospace manufacturer Embraer, ending his tenure there as Vice President of Sales for their Executive Jet division based in Dubai.

After returning to his home country of Brazil to work for a business jet start-up when he noticed the work that Heart Aerospace was doing. "The opportunity of working on the design of a new aeroplane," Camelier said, "especially one that is so innovative and that is breaking convention in terms of propulsion systems and emissions characteristics—that really, really caught my attention."

Heart Aerospace continued to recruit, hiring more Brazilian Embraer alums alongside employees from a total of 25 countries. Though the result was a patchwork of workplace cultures, the team has gelled by bringing the best elements from their past experience to create something all their own.

"You have to work like hell," Camelier said, "but it's also extremely exciting to do something new."

While many of the Brazilian staff still prefer the beaches of Florianopolis to the winter snow of Gothenburg—even after Anders took the team on a ski trip to the Arctic—the transition has otherwise been relatively smooth. "Gothenburg is a very advanced city and Sweden is a very advanced society," he said. "So other than the weather, it's been easy to adapt."

THE FIRST MAJOR SALE OF 200 PLANES FROM AN EMAIL THAT WAS ALMOST MISSED

In their Y Combinator pitch, Anders and Klara presented Heart as a solution for the Nordics, with potential use for wider markets in the future, even if it was somewhat speculative—but enquiries from outside of Scandinavia came sooner than expected.

So soon, in fact, that the team almost missed one in 2021.

"Klara came to me and said, 'I found something in the inbox,'" Anders said. "I googled the names and they looked legitimate and that it might actually be something. But first of all, it seemed strange."

Though the email had come to the generic company address, it was marked as from United Airlines and its regional partner, Mesa and turned out to be legitimate. After some coordination and a few meetings, the connection resulted in an investment and an order for 200 planes.

Soon, Heart was getting approached from companies as far afield as Canada and New Zealand. Because travel restrictions were beginning to lift again after the COVID-19 pandemic, airlines were finding themselves under the climate change spotlight once again, and Heart's aircraft seemed to offer a solution for shorter regional routes.

All of a sudden, the ES-19 was no longer going to be an aircraft that would just be flying over the Norwegian fjords. It would be used for regional flights all over the world, just as they had suggested at Y Combinator.

With the ES-19, they had an aircraft that truly had worldwide appeal, which led Anders and the growing team at Heart Aerospace to wonder: *Would their little 19-seat aircraft really be suitable for so many new customers?* As more potential customers approached Heart, the answer seemed to be "maybe not."

"They were saying, 'Yes, a 19-seat aeroplane is very nice," Camelier said, "but you know, if it was a bit larger and had more luggage capacity, that would have an even bigger appeal.'" The airlines Heart spoke to wanted greater route flexibility; in particular, they wanted more range, which would add to the weight of the aircraft.

Aside from its size-related limitations, the ES-19's range was also limited by strict operating rules, including having 45 minutes of reserve power available and being 100 nautical miles from alternative airports in case of emergency. As a result, the nominal 400 km range of the ES-19 was going to end up closer to 150 km in reality, a massive reduction that would greatly restrict the aircraft's potential.

In addition to having a product plan that wouldn't perform as well as the team originally imagined, they also were being pressured to deliver an aircraft that could perform *even better* than what they had initially proposed on paper. All the same, the Heart Aerospace team decided to treat the challenges as an opportunity: What if they could modify their initial designs in order to create a product they could sell to a potentially even bigger market?

Though the original intention was to run the ES-19 through the European's CS-23 certification for small aircraft, the team now aimed higher, seeking CS-25 certification, the next category up (equivalent to class 25 in the US).

They looked into providing the greater flexibility airlines

wanted as well, namely increased range, more room for passengers and additional space for luggage.

By the end of their revisions, the ES-19 was put to bed and new plans for the ES-30 were born: a longer-range plane which the Heart Aerospace team built a new airframe for just in time for the company's "Hangar Day", or annual general meeting, in September 2022.

Although building a larger and more complex aircraft meant their go-live date needed to push from 2026 to 2028, the company decided it was a sacrifice worth making to bring their technology to a larger market.

In all, the vision was coming into focus: by the end of the decade, passengers all around the world would be flying in Heart Aerospace's aircraft.

All the same, reworking the ES-19 design was no small task.

A DELICATE MARRIAGE OF CUTTING-EDGE INNOVATION AND FAMILIARITY IN THE ES-30 REGIONAL AEROPLANE

As the name suggests, the ES-30 will hold 30 passengers in a two plus one seating configuration when it comes to market, all with an industry standard 30-inch pitch. The aircraft will feature a fully pressurised cabin with a standing aisle as well as overhead bins for small carry-ons. For airlines, there is also the option to order aircraft with a small galley and WC at the front.

For passengers already used to flying on regional aircraft, they will likely find the experience on the ES-30 a familiar one, which Anders said that this was deliberate.[12] "A passenger shouldn't feel that this is a downgrade from what they are used to. Instead, it should feel like an upgrade". To that point, one very noticeable improvement that passengers will experience first-hand are the lower noise levels.

Regional turboprops have the reputation of being noisy when sitting in the cabin. By contrast, the ES-30 will be quiet. The electric motor means taxiing will be silent, while take-off and landing will involve little noise, all of which is a major benefit not only for passengers but for communities near regional airports as well.

Similarly, the ES-30 was designed in a way that regional operators would immediately find comfortable to operate, despite it being a brand new plane.

Again, this design choice was intentional. "We have to manage and limit the amount of innovation that we deploy, especially in the regional airline market," Pippard said. "Those customers don't pay for shiny objects in the cockpit. They pay for the return on investment."

More specifically, the return those airlines are looking for is reliable aircraft that can still be commercially attractive and easy to operate while also delivering an ultra-low carbon footprint.

While the ES-30 will still feature cutting edge technology and design features—including a fully glass cockpit, an all-digital system, a digital fly-by-wire and a state of the art de-icing system allowing pilots to fly in any weather condition—none of the innovation will get in the way of familiarity and practicality.

"LIARS, DAMN LIARS AND BATTERY SUPPLIERS" AND THE FRUSTRATING LIMITS OF AVIATION INNOVATION

Though Heart Aerospace calls the ES-30 an electric aircraft, strictly speaking, it is hybrid-electric, having fuel-powered turbines as well as a battery motor, a technology Anders calls "reserve hybrid."

The batteries sit under the aircraft by the landing gear and feed power to four electric motors on the main wings, and there are two turbine generators at the back of the aircraft fed by fuel tanks. Though the latter won't be turned on for many shorter flights, resulting in true-zero emissions flights, they are there for airlines who need the ability to fly greater distances.

When running on battery power only, the range of the ES-30 is 200km. Using hybrid-electric power, that range increases to

400 km. Airlines even have the option of removing five seats out of the ES-30, reducing passenger capacity to 25 and effectively redoubling potential flight distance to 800 km.

The ES-30 will be the first in a family of regional aircraft, but Anders plans to start developing a 50-seat aircraft, the ES-50, once battery technology improves. When that happens, Heart's aircraft would be positioned to become the low-to-no carbon alternative to larger regional turboprops or smaller regional jets. But as with solving any technical problem in aviation, improving electric batteries is not as easy as it sounds.

Historically speaking, one of the biggest barriers for the development of electric and hybrid-electric aircraft companies has been the limitations of battery capacity. According to Pippard, the process of designing the ES-30 has been no exception.

"Our battery partner (BAE Systems)[13] came out with a good saying," he said. " 'In the world, there are liars, damn liars and battery suppliers.'" As he explains, electric battery capacity is constrained by three intersecting curves: energy density, power density and battery life.

"The laws of physics say you can pick any two," Pippard said, "but everyone is out there with outlandish and outrageous claims when it comes to batteries." To suit its customers and their own environmental mission, Heart Aerospace has decided to focus on energy density and battery life cycle.

According to a July 2022 paper on electric aviation by the International Council on Clean Transportation (ICCT),[14] an electric aircraft carrying nine passengers could probably travel a distance of 140 km safely at the time of writing, though they added that hypothetically possible improvements in battery technology might make it possible for a 90-seat aircraft to safely fly 280km, a staggering improvement.

Though Pippard maintains some healthy scientific scepticism, he is also optimistic that there are many promising battery-related developments in the pipeline. NASA, for example, is busy developing a project called SABERS (Solid-state Architecture Batteries for Enhanced Rechargeability and Safety),[15] which uses new technology to achieve targeted properties for power, energy, safety, packaging and scalability. In an October, 2022 NASA media statement, SABERS' principal investigator Rocco Viggiano said the project was "a new frontier of battery research," the possibilities of which were "pretty incredible."[16]

In the private sector, entrepreneurs looking at the issue include Richard Wang, who *Time Magazine*[17] profiled alongside his start-up company Cuberg, which is now owned by Swedish company Northvolt (Peter Carlsson, Northvolt's CEO, is an advisor to Heart Aerospace).[18]

With a focus on aviation, Wang is trying to develop lithium metal, as opposed to lithium ion batteries, which would result in 70% more energy per unit of weight and volume compared to the batteries in use today.

According to Pippard, lithium metal is seeming to be the "next big thing" in the field of electric batteries. Even so, projects like Cuberg's and NASA's SABERS will take a while to come to fruition—too long for Heart Aerospace's team to wait to deliver an aircraft. As a result, the team decided to equip the ES-30 with a reserve hybrid system, allowing the aircraft a range of anywhere from 200 km (when using battery power alone) up to 800 km on hybrid energy. In any case, the sustainability benefits for airlines will be significant.

An all-electric flight will be zero carbon, and a hybrid electric one will have at least 50% lower emissions—more if airlines use Sustainable Aviation Fuel (SAF) to power the turbines. But while all of this is important, sustainability benefits alone are not what's driving all the major orders that Heart is fielding from airlines.

Ultimately, airline bosses still chase profit and have a responsibility to their shareholders to maximise the value of their shares.

Even so, this is another area where Heart Aerospace thrives.

According to Sacca, the true value that Heart delivers comes from one thing: "making unprofitable routes profitable."

SOLVING THE COMPLEX ECONOMICS OF REGIONAL AVIATION TO MAKE "UNPROFITABLE ROUTES PROFITABLE" AGAIN

There's a map that Anders Forslund likes to bring out at aviation conferences that shows the large number of regional routes served by smaller aircraft in the USA during the mid-1990s. It was particularly instrumental in a conversation Anders had with Mesa Airlines CEO Jonathan Orstein.

Mesa Airlines flies regional flights for United under the United brand, and as Orstein told Forslund in one of their presale meetings, many of the routes on the map are now gone, resulting in a lot of US airports losing their commercial air service links. Often, those routes have changed or disappeared for no reason other than the unfavourable economics of regional aviation.

For airlines, the operating costs of maintaining smaller aircraft that carry fewer passengers are comparatively high; there are also noise and emissions concerns to consider when flying into certain smaller, regional airports in semi-residential areas.

Since many of those destinations don't see a lot of traffic and the complexity of maintaining them is so high, many airlines stop running them altogether to cut costs and maintain the integrity of their other routes. Fortunately, this is the exact problem that Heart Aerospace is positioned to solve, a fact that Anders was told again and again in sales meetings with airline CEOs.

"I kept hearing, 'You guys are underselling this," Anders said. "This is the big thing. We stopped flying these 19 seater and 30 seater routes because of the cost of the engines."

Mesa Airlines underscored their point in a press release announcing their 100 aircraft order from Heart Aerospace.[19]

They gave the specific example of an airport in Farmington, New Mexico, a rural community bordering the Navajo Nation that once had 30 daily departures to seven destinations but no longer had a commercial airline link for economic reasons. Even so, thanks to their ES-30 purchase order, Mesa Airlines said it was a route that they might be able to restore.

Compared to standard aircraft with combustion engines, electric aircraft are cheaper to maintain; they save airlines money on fuel costs, and they don't disrupt local communities as a result of their lower noise and emissions. NASA summarised the effect of this new development succinctly in its April 2021 Regional Air Mobility (RAM) Report:

> *The local airport you may not even have known existed will soon be a catalyst for change in how you travel . . . RAM will operate aircraft so quiet and unobtrusive, and provide services so accessible and useful, that stakeholders will want RAM flights in their communities.*

STRATEGIC DESIGN FOR A PLANE OF THE FUTURE THAT SLOTS INTO REGIONAL ROUTES OF THE PRESENT

Though the potential to revive dormant regional routes and create new ones in the future is promising, what about the regional aviation network of today?

Here, the Heart ES-30 proves its utility by slotting easily onto existing routes, which can be illustrated by looking at United's hub in Chicago O'Hare, with the context that United Airlines is a Heart investor and partner.

Currently, United's regional arm, United Express, operates a number of very short flights into O'Hare. On their own, the economics of those flights often make little sense, but the value to the airline comes by feeding passengers onto flights going to other United destinations, including ones outside the United States.

As a result, United Express operates six to seven flights a day from Milwaukee, the largest city in the neighbouring state of Wisconsin, into Chicago O'Hare, even though the actual distance between those two airports is only 108 km or 67 miles. Similarly, Wisconsin's capital, Madison, has six flights a day into Chicago O'Hare via United Express, with a distance of only 175 km or 109 miles.

United Express uses a mix of aircraft on these routes, very often regional jets like the CRJ-550 and the ERJ-145, each with around 50 seats. At peak times, larger aircraft such as an Airbus A319 are also used.

According to the ICAO,[20] the average fuel burn for a round trip from Madison, Wisconsin to Chicago O'Hare is 2220.7 kg. With six round trips a day or 2190 a year for United, that's a total fuel burn of almost 5000 metric tonnes. It is in regional negotiations like this that Heart's ES-30 proves to be an economic breakthrough.

Since Madison to Chicago is less than 200 km, United could switch to flying those routes with the ES-30 on electric power only, for considerable savings on fuel.

Of course, with 30 seats, the ES-30 doesn't have the same capacity as the aircraft currently operating those routes—but like so many things in sustainable aviation, what appears to be a problem is in fact an opportunity to rethink how regional aviation works.

Airlines could, for example, operate these routes on a high frequency "turn up and go" model, an idea that was once suggested by Air New Zealand CEO Greg Foran at the APEX/IFSA EXPO in Long Beach, California in 2022.[21] While considering the potential in electric aircraft, Foran wondered if certain regional routes could be programmed differently:

Thinking about it like an Uber, it's basically just shuttling backwards and forwards—and it's maybe going every 30 minutes and you just turn up and pay for it when you get on the plane. Why not?

In other words, you could create low-noise, high frequency electric aircraft shuttles powered by renewable energy, between two points.

IMPROVING HUB CONGESTION AND OPENING THE GLOBAL SOUTH WITH NIMBLE AIRCRAFT LIKE THE ES-30

Of course, there are two other ways the ES-30 could transform regional aviation.

For a United States-based example, instead of having every regional flight to or from Wisconsin, Illinois and Indiana go through United's busy Chicago O'Hare hub, completing more point-to-point traffic with smaller aircraft will become possible.

But if we look to the so-called Global South, the impact of aircraft like the ES-30 could be even greater.

"We'll have early adopters like the Nordics or North America or New Zealand," said Anders, "but the biggest impact will be in places where actually there are no planes right now."

For this, Anders gives the example of Indonesia, a country of 17,000 islands that is ten times the size of all the Nordic countries combined. Air travel in Indonesia has quadrupled in the past decade, yet most of the country is as yet still unserved by commercial aviation. All of this means one thing: most Indonesians don't fly.

When talking about the possible electric aviation revolution in the global South, Anders uses the analogy of mobile phones.

His native Nordics were pioneers in the development of mobile phone standards, with companies like Nokia and Ericsson innovating and driving the pace. All the same, the real mobile revolution happened in developing countries.

Landlines require infrastructure in terms of cables to the local community and then into people's homes. As a result, most people never had one.

Instead they went straight to using mobile phones, with often very cheap data and calling rates, and where the only infrastructure required was a cell tower to serve the local area.

This shift, among other things, led to a lot of African countries being ahead of the Global North in mobile payments. Countries like Kenya had services such as the M-Pesa long before mobile payment apps like Venmo existed in Europe and North America.

Anders believes that the same thing could be true of electric aviation. With new aircraft like the ES-30, communities in Africa or South East Asia wouldn't need expensive airport infrastructure complete with fuel pipelines. Instead, a simple charging station, quite possibly solar-powered, would do.

All of these changes would have socio-economic as well as environmental benefits, all of which help to answer the common criticism that increasing air travel will only harm the environment, or that it will be something only richer countries benefit from.

HEART AEROSPACE'S FUTURE "SONGBOOK" OF AVIATION

Not surprisingly, industry interest in Heart Aerospace has been considerable.

United Airlines has invested in Heart Aerospace and ordered 100 aircraft along with Mesa and both have included the option to buy 100 more. Air Canada has invested as well with an order of 30 ES-30s, while Swedish aerospace and defence giant Saab has come on as minority shareholder.[22]

On the other side of the world, Air New Zealand selected Heart Aerospace as a long-term partner for their Mission Next Gen Aircraft partnership, with the goal of replacing their Q300 domestic fleet.[23] Other potential orders have come from Braathens Regional Airlines (BRA), Icelandair, SAS, Portugal's Seve-nair and New Zealand's Sounds Air, and additional institutional investors include Bill Gates' Breakthrough Energy Ventures.

Through it all, Heart's team of almost 200 has grown to fill their once-empty hangar, generating huge media interest in the process. When the company unveiled the ES-30 at their Hangar Day event, it led to US-based talk show host Trevor Noah doing a spot on the ES-30 on Comedy Central's *The Daily Show*.

In the segment, Noah joked about the pilot having to ask passengers for their battery charging packs mid-air, ironically using the analogy of a mobile phone that hasn't charged prop-erly. It was probably the first time that millions of Americans were exposed to the coming reality of electric aviation.

In a sector with dozens of start-ups, most of which have little to show in terms of funding or pre-orders, Heart has both—as well as a hybrid-electric plane which will save airlines money, rejuvenate regional aviation and slot easily into existing fleets and schedules, all while offering significant environmental benefits.

All of this has added to the company's momentum and success, making the ES-30 a relatively easy sell (even if it wasn't an easy build). Even so, their groundbreaking plan is only setting the tone for what's to come, a first song in a future anthol-ogy. Once again, Anders reverts to a musical metaphor.

"The ES-30 is like a song that I think we can play," he said, "but I'm not trying to write an opera out of it."

1. **Don't be afraid to follow your dreams.** Remember the famous Steve Jobs quote: "Do you want to sell sugar water for the rest of your life or come with me and change the world?" Anders Forslund, like many other people in this book, found himself at a career and life crossroads. Rather than go down a well-trodden road where he would have been following others, he took a chance on his big idea, which made a huge difference.

2. **Improvise where necessary.** With limited funds, Heart Aerospace designed to design and "build" their aircraft on CAD software so they could come to Y Combinator with a 3D model of the aircraft, rather than spending much more to build it in the real world. Similarly, when airlines wanted more range and capabilities, they scrapped plans for the ES-19 and designed the ES-30 instead. As their story shows, successful start-ups must be able to pivot and improvise.

3. **Don't be afraid to ask for things, especially if you have nothing to lose.** Anders told us that with nothing to lose, he and Klara found the confidence to approach three Scandinavian airlines to secure Letter of Intents (LOIs) that would help them land an investment at Y Combinator's Demo Day. Though it was an unproven and unorthodox plan, it was the best one they had and they had nothing to lose and everything to gain. As a result of their bold actions, they walked away with not one but three LOIs and successfully secured the investment they needed.

4. **"The tiniest team can build something massive."** As Chris Sacca said, good ideas and innovative processes using the latest technology can make up for having a large team. In certain industries, being an efficient

underdog can be an advantage—this can be especially true in aviation.

5. **Don't discount experience.** Running an aviation start-up is nothing like running a software start-up. You need experienced hands on board. While in usual circumstances this would seem difficult, offering people the opportunity to do something truly transformational is very motivating, and experienced hands will join you. This is something we saw again and again while researching this book.

6. **Don't overcomplicate things for the customer.** Despite using hybrid-electric propulsion systems, Heart has developed a product that's easy for airline customers to understand and that fits into their current needs. Both of these things make it easier for them to buy.

7. **What's the big picture?** When Anders and Klara Forslund appeared in front of Y Combinator, they pitched a short-term opportunity in the Nordics—but they also sold investors a bigger vision of the entire world flying in electric aircraft. Though the second part of the pitch was largely speculative and aspirational, by keeping that vision as their "true north" across many different business decisions, their regional plan began to turn into a global one, just as they said it would.

TWO
ZEROAVIA: HYDROGEN-ELECTRIC ENGINES AND BUILDING A "CITY OF AVIATION" TO ENABLE A TRUE-ZERO FUTURE

AS A PILOT with over three decades of both commercial and military experience, Jon Killerby is proud of his career in aviation. But the more he's learned about environmental sustainability over the years, the more uneasy he's become.

Killerby even has a presentation that he refers to when people ask about his job. It includes a slide full of pictures of the different types of aircraft that he's flown.

At the top of it is a large headline:

That's a lot of carbon, Jon!

Killerby's journey towards burning all that carbon began as a teenager, when he started at the bottom rung of the aviation industry ladder as a "hangar rat," responsible for cleaning the aircraft and sweeping floors.

Killerby subsequently built a distinguished career in Britain's Royal Air Force (RAF), where he piloted fighter jets such as the Tornado and even got a chance to fly the B2 Stealth Bomber with the US Air Force as an exchange officer. Following that, he moved into commercial aviation.

Still, after all his many years of experience, Killerby began to feel that his career had peaked.

He was approaching his own personal crossroads when, in

the autumn of 2021, he got a call from a startup called ZeroAvia, whose mission is to decarbonise aviation by equipping aircraft with a new and revolutionary kind of engine.

Through the interview process and his own research, he learned that the job would mostly take place in the English countryside and wouldn't involve flying the kinds of big, powerful aircraft he was used to.

Instead, he'd be flying smaller, 19-seat turboprops.

As Killerby learned, what sets ZeroAvia's aircraft apart is that they don't burn fossil fuels. Instead, they are powered by a combination of hydrogen and electric batteries, producing zero greenhouse gas emissions.

After hearing all this, Killerby was presented with what he calls a "once in a career" opportunity: to be the Chief Test Pilot of these experimental aircraft which had the potential to change commercial air travel forever.

"It was a no-brainer, really," Killerby said—especially because at ZeroAvia, he is "very proud" to explain the purpose of his work when he comes home to his two young sons.

As it turns out, it's a motivating factor that Killerby and Val Miftakhov, the founder and CEO of ZeroAvia, have in common.

VAL MIFTAKHOV'S ENTREPRENEURIAL ORIGINS

Though he's been living in the United States for over 25 years, Miftakhov grew up in Siberia (in what was then the Soviet Union). In 1997, he moved to the US to study at Princeton University to get his PhD in Physics and became interested in sustainability early on.

"I want my children to look back at this time and say that their dad did as much as possible to solve the problems we had," Miftakhov said, "and that now, we live in a better place."

After spells at McKinsey and Google, Miftakhov took to entrepreneurship and founded eMotorWerks, a company that now powers the world's largest network of smart charging stations for electric cars.

In order to grow, eMotorWorks had to address a variety of common customer objections and overcome logistical challenges; it is perhaps where some of Miftakhov's signature approach of meeting people and problems where they are began to take shape.

As Miftakhov explains, electric car owners often face a common accusation when it comes to the "sustainability" of their vehicles, namely that the electricity they use is produced by charging stations primarily powered by burning coal and other fossil fuels.

Thus, Miftakhov's aim with eMotorWerks was not only to create the infrastructure to charge electric cars; it was also to address that criticism by maximising the renewable energy that went into each one.

When energy company Enel acquired eMotorWerks in 2017, Miftakhov had become a seasoned leader and was ready for a new challenge—and as a former pilot, aviation was as close to Miftakhov's heart as decarbonisation was.[1]

Given that aviation's share of global emissions was actually *increasing* as other industries were beginning to wean themselves off fossil fuels, Miftakhov knew how far the industry had to go to become sustainable.

"The power sector is on a good trajectory, the ground transportation sector is on a good trajectory, and everyone is building electric cars," Miftakhov said.

As these major climate change agents become smaller and smaller in terms of emissions, aviation's contribution becomes larger and larger. And then you have the fact that the industry is growing."

To Miftakhov, decarbonisation is an incredibly urgent goal —and the window of opportunity is closing fast. "The typical lifetime of a commercial aircraft is 30 years," Miftakhov said. "If you want to be zero emission by 2050, you have less than one generation of aircraft to do it. So we are already late."

After thinking it through, Miftakhov had a new horizon he'd set his sights on. In 2017, he founded ZeroAvia, headquartered in Hollister, California, as his next venture—and though the company has taken a pragmatic and strategic approach to their mission, they certainly aren't skimping on utopian vision.

Miftakhov's goal is not "net-zero" aviation where emissions are offset by other beneficial activities but otherwise still exist residually; it is "true-zero" aviation, meaning aircraft that don't emit *any* dangerous environmental pollutants.

To achieve his goal, ZeroAvia is dedicated to developing hydrogen-electric engines and powertrains that can be fitted to aircraft that are in the skies *right now*, with ambitions of bringing their technology to commercial flights as early as 2025.

CHARTING A FLIGHT PATH OUT OF THE "VALLEY OF DEATH"

To solve aviation's sustainability problem, next generation aircraft companies are taking a wide range of approaches.

Some are making their own aircraft from the ground up; others are choosing to develop technology that can be retrofitted into existing fleets or used by existing manufacturers.

While each approach has its pros and cons, ZeroAvia has decided that working with existing manufacturers is the best path forward for its own stratospheric aims.[2]

As it relates to production speed, working with existing aircraft is much faster than starting from scratch for both development and certification.

Though ZeroAvia's engines will need to be certified by regulators such as the United States's FAA or the European Union's EASA, that process will be made much less onerous by attaching their new power systems to aircraft and technology that have been certified by regulatory bodies in the past.

Certification for new technology that doesn't build off *any*

existing components comes to regulators without any established prior context, and thus has much more to prove and takes
more time.

Cost was another key factor behind the decision; after all,
developing and manufacturing a brand new plane from the
ground up requires an enormous amount of upfront capital
investment.

According to former Wisk CEO Gary Gysin, an aviation
company developing electric vertical take-off and landing
(eVTOL) aircraft to be used as self-flying taxis, the upfront
investment needed to execute the company's mission is approximately $2 billion.[3]

In his *Sustainability in the Air* podcast interview with
Shashank Nigam, Boom Supersonic CEO Blake Scholl cited an
even bigger figure: to get his company's own new plane in the
air would require an eye-watering $8 billion.[4]

Though there are differences in complexity between Wisk's
aircraft and Boom Supersonic, both figures provide a sense of
scale.

It's the reason why, out of the hundreds of next generation
aircraft manufacturers that exist today, so few will emerge from
the so-called "Valley of Death," a term used by venture capital-
ists for the period of time when a start-up is growing by
burning investment capital but is not yet generating any
revenue.

For their part, ZeroAvia intends to be out of that valley
sooner rather than later by earning revenue from entry-level
engines once they are certified in 2025 and reinvesting to further
develop their technology.

While many of ZeroAvia's earliest decisions were driven by
manufacturing and ecosystem-building concerns, Miftakhov
says he and his team were also driven by what they saw as a
sales opportunity offered by a "plug and play" approach—
particularly because today's aircraft already require so much
ongoing maintenance.

"In existing fleets," Miftakhov said, "people go through the engines and have to replace them in major maintenance events."

It's for this inevitable moment that he has positioned his company: instead of trying to prolong the life of an existing fossil-fuel based engine, why not go slightly further and prolong the life of the entire aircraft by replacing the entire fuel system with ZeroAvia's zero emissions, cheaper-to-operate powertrain?

As Miftakhov explains, the benefit to airlines will be like getting a brand new plane at a fraction of the usual cost.

Additionally, ZeroAvia is looking into offering their airline manufacturing customers the option of having their powertrains installed at the point of production, otherwise known as "line fitting." At time of writing, ZeroAvia's partners include DeHavilland Canada and Mitsubishi Heavy Industries, which will eventually see their technology installed in Dash-8 turboprops and the Canadair series of regional jets, respectively.

"I didn't want to have to compete with all these great people who built all these great aeroplanes with decades worth of experience," Miftakhov said. "I wanted to partner with those folks rather than compete with them. They have relationships with the customers, and they can also help sell our engines."

In sum, Miftakhov believes his approach will allow everyone involved to keep doing what they do best, and without getting in one another's way. For ZeroAvia, that means pouring their focus into perfecting aviation's next generation of engines.

THE BEST-FIT SOLUTION OF HYDROGEN-ELECTRIC POWERED ENGINES— AND WHY INVESTORS ARE TAKING NOTICE

In aviation, hydrogen-electric power, often referred to as hydrogen fuel cell technology, uses a series of interconnected processes to power an aircraft.

Hydrogen is stored on the aircraft and fed to fuel cells. The fuel cells convert the hydrogen into electricity and heat. The electricity is then used to power the aircraft engines.

The only by-products of this process are water and heat, making it a clean and sustainable way to power an aircraft.

The technology ZeroAvia is developing currently uses hydrogen as a gas, though the company intends to transition to liquid hydrogen in the future, which will be necessary in order to power 50+ seat aircraft.

Still, a common question that seems to arise here is: wouldn't it be simpler just to use hydrogen as a combustible fuel source in modified jet engines?

It is an approach a number of other major industry players are adopting, including Rolls Royce and Airbus, the latter of which plans to have a 100-200-seat hydrogen-powered aircraft in the skies by 2035.[5]

ZeroAvia and other companies going down the hydrogen-electric route say that hydrogen turbines still produce nitrogen oxides and significant amounts of contrails, both of which are air pollutants.

For companies focused on sustainability, particularly since two thirds of aviation's climate impact is estimated to come from non-CO2 emissions, any technology that would greatly increase that impact in the long-run understandably causes concern.[6]

Of course, hydrogen-electric technology has its own limitations, most significant among them the weight of its "power plants," the technology needed to build into an aircraft to generate and route hydrogen-electric power to its engines.

Adding weight to an aircraft has a significant impact on how many passengers a plane can carry, as well as how far it can safely fly. Even so, Miftakhov believes the long-term benefits of hydrogen-electric power are more than worth the inconvenience of any short-term obstacles (some of which ZeroAvia is already working on resolving).

In particular, Miftakhov believes that having ZeroAvia build aeroplane engines that result in no CO2 or NOx emissions are good to position the company in a competitive field while adding major momentum to a sustainable future of aviation relatively quickly.

Of course, there's also a more market-driven factor behind ZeroAvia's multi-layered strategy: hydrogen-electric aircraft are very cost effective to operate and maintain. The company estimates that its powertrain will deliver a reduction of 40% in operating costs, including fuel and maintenance savings.

All of this, of course, adds up to a very compelling offer for end customers and aircraft operators alike—and it has made many countless big-name investors take notice.

Just as Miftakhov understands the urgency of making aviation more environmentally sustainable, Bill Gates' Breakthrough Energy, a venture fund aimed at supporting companies that will help transition the planet to net-zero, also agrees that the time for small steps has passed.

As such, Breakthrough Energy has a very high bar to clear when it comes to its investment: any company in its portfolio should be able to mitigate half a gigaton of greenhouse gas emissions annually. "That's about one percent of annual emissions," Matt Eggers, a partner at the fund, said. "It's a really big number for any individual company."[7]

It's significant, then, that Breakthrough Energy has invested in ZeroAvia—and that Eggers has held a seat on the company's board. "It has the potential to be one of the key companies that gets us through the transition to a zero-carbon world," he said.

Today, ZeroAvia's list of partners and backers reads almost like a who's who of the venture capital and aviation community.

Investors include both Bill Gates' Breakthrough Energy Fund[8] and Amazon's Climate Pledge Fund,[9] as well as other major airlines[10] including British Airways and Iberia owner IAG, United Airlines, Alaska Airlines, and American Airlines.[11]

Other organisations committed to fund ZeroAvia include Saudi Arabia's futuristic NEOM development, German climate technology fund AENU, Shell Ventures and Barclay's Sustainable Capital Investment Vehicle.

Meanwhile, ZeroAvia has benefited from UK Government support through the U.K. Aerospace Technology Institute and its HyFlyer 1 and HyFlyer 2 grants. This is one reason why its primary test facility is in the UK despite being headquartered in California.

Initially, the company's test facility was located at Cranfield Airport in Hertfordshire, but now, test flights are being run out of Cotswolds Airport in Kemble, Gloucestershire.

What all of ZeroAvia's backers seem to have in common is simple: They are inspired by Miftakhov's vision and are confident the company can actually take the necessary steps to execute it. "So many companies say that they will change the world," Eggers said, "but this is a company that actually will."[12]

ATTRACTING AVIATION HEAVY HITTERS WHO ARE HELPING TO TURN THE DREAM INTO REALITY

In addition to A-list investors, Miftakhov has succeeded in attracting a team of industry veterans to help turn his vision into reality.

Like Miftakhov, all of them hope to use their experience to do something about it, proving ZeroAvia's bold "true-zero" vision of aviation to be a powerful marketing tool for top-tier talent all around the world.

One example is Gabriele Teofili, ZeroAvia's managing director. Originally from Italy, Teofili is an aerospace engineer by training with more than 20 years' experience, including stints at major companies such as helicopter maker Leonardo and aircraft manufacturer Airbus.

Before joining ZeroAvia in early 2022, Teofili was living in Munich with his wife and 12-year-old daughter, working as the head of engine manufacturer Rolls Royce's urban air mobility business.

Just like Chief Test Pilot Killerby, Teofili didn't hesitate when opportunity came knocking. "I had done everything I'd ever dreamed of in my career," Teofili said, "and I wanted to invest all the confidence, competence and experience I had acquired into something that [wasn't only] good for *me*."

Though he knew it would be an adjustment for his family, particularly for his young daughter, who would need to make new friends. After discussing it together, his family fully supported his decision—and he got his daughter's blessing. "She knows that what her Papa is going to do is important," Teofili said.

In the space of four days, Teofili and his family packed their things, sold their Munich apartment and drove from Munich to ZeroAvia's base in the Cotswolds, where he and his family now live.

HOW AN EARLY FORCED LANDING LED TO ZEROAVIA'S REDESIGNED TEST PILOT PROGRAMME

Of course, even with so much support and careful planning, every new aviation company eventually has to step over a threshold of incredible risk. After all, eventually, someone needs to leave the ground while flying untested technology.

And so in September 2020, ZeroAvia made history when a Piper Malibu Mirage successfully flew for eight minutes, using ZeroAvia's experimental ZA250 powertrain. [13]

It was the world's first successful flight in a passenger aircraft using hydrogen-electric technology.

The flight test programme carried on without any incidents until April 29th, 2021. That afternoon, a Piper Malibu Mirage with both a pilot and flight observer on board took off from Cranfield Airport.

After take-off, there was a gap between switching from battery to fuel cell power, the propeller windmilled and became a generator, forcing the inverters to lock out to prevent over voltage, thus preventing the system from operating on fuel cell power. As a result, the pilot had to make a forced landing.

Fortunately, there were no fatalities or injuries, but it was a sobering moment for the company, and for Miftakhov in particular.

The UK's Air Accidents Investigation Branch (AAIB) published its final report on the flight a year later in 2022 and concluded that the hydrogen itself wasn't a factor in the crash.[14] Instead, the error had been human and procedural.

The shift from one power system to another was done at the wrong point," Miftakhov said. "The sequence of actions by the crew was not really optimal." In the aftermath, he and his team took stock of how the accident could've happened.

On the plus side, the incident had been the company's only testing accident thus far, and it had been non-fatal; the only damage was to the aircraft.

Because of that (and somewhat ironically), the crash had demonstrated how *safe* their technology was, if it demonstrated anything. The biggest negative was as obvious as, well, a plane crash—but it revealed a subtle detail and an opportunity to prevent any similar issues in the future.

Up until that point, ZeroAvia had been using a pool of many experienced pilots to run their test flights, though they now saw their approach was perhaps adding a confounding variable to their experiments.

To remedy that, ZeroAvia made a decision to hire a full-time, dedicated Chief Test Pilot. This, of course, is how the aforementioned Killerby came on board.

Killerby's arrival coincided with ZeroAvia taking a delivery of a Dornier-228 aircraft from regional airline Aurigny.

Unlike the Piper Malibu, which was used to test the experimental ZA250 engine, the Dornier aircraft would be used to test the ZA600 powertrain, ZeroAvia's first commercial product.

As a result, these flight tests are critical, and Killerby was able to be involved right from the beginning.

This was helpful, Killerby explains, because in the best cases, a dedicated test pilot offers a twofold benefit. "There's the element of experience in the aircraft," he said, "but added to that, you need to have someone who can manage and design your flight test programme to do it safely."

Over the subsequent months, Killerby took ZeroAvia's aircraft through a series of ground tests, leading up to high speed taxis on the runway, before it was ready to fly.

In addition to having a dedicated flight testing department, ZeroAvia was also mindful that a subtle mechanical issue might've been partially responsible for the difficulty of toggling between power systems on their April 29th test flight.

As such, the company also began building up its maintenance operations and reviewed its processes to ensure they were following all best practises and aviation principles.

All of their efforts were especially important because they were approaching a mission-critical hurdle: ZeroAvia needed to get the nod from regulators, first in North America and Europe and then in other parts of the world.

The first step in that process involved successfully convincing the UK's Civil Aviation Authority (CAA) to greenlight their next series of test flights out of Cotswold Airport[15]—tests which had much stricter conditions than those needed for earlier flights with six-seater aircraft, since these involved the 19-seat Dornier-228.

Taken all together, everything seemed to signify the maturity of the company's processes and design approaches. It was now time to proceed toward full commercial certification of its power plants.

ZEROAVIA'S DO-OR-DIE TEST FLIGHT TO CERTIFY THEIR POWERTRAIN

The Civil Aviation Authority gave ZeroAvia the go-ahead to test the Dornier-228 before Christmas; however, thanks to the British winter weather of clouds and rain, the big day was delayed again and again.

"I have learned the meaning of resilience," said Gabriele

Teofili, "because we had been attempting to fly since the 21st of December."

"Every single morning, we would go out there with the *Top Gun* music in our heads, thinking it was going to happen," he said, "and every single evening, we would come back and it didn't happen. For almost a month, there was not a single day which was suitable because it was raining every single day."

On the morning of Wednesday, January 18, there was fog in the morning but no rain; in the afternoon, the sun had started to burn through the sky.

After waiting so long for a window of opportunity, Teofili was eager to push ahead. "We were thinking, 'Okay Jon, let's go out and finally make this bloody first flight!' And of course Jon, being the most responsible person at that moment, waited one more day."

Sure enough, the weather held until the next day, Thursday, January 19th, and the rest of the ZeroAvia team was ready to watch the flight from the restaurant adjoining the air field—everyone, that is, except Teofili. "I was in the corner," he said. "I was too tense."

As the culmination of a lot of effort by ZeroAvia's entire team, it was an understandably big moment—and when the plane successfully took off, the feeling was almost euphoric. Even so, a successful take-off was still only half of the test.

"We were all screaming," Teofili said, "but the aerospace people weren't doing anything, because the most important thing is the landing, not the take-off."

Flying in the cockpit alongside Killerby was ZeroAvia flight test engineer James Yapp, who says the engines were performing spectacularly. "Everything that we predicted would happen, happened," Yapp said. "We always knew it was going to fly. It was just a question of when."

After 10 minutes, Killerby and Yapp circled around to come in for the landing, and the entire ZeroAvia team's hearts were in their throats.

Sure enough, the Dornier-228 touched down smoothly and without incident, and the ground team was elated. "The weather was perfect," said Killerby. "The aircraft was perfect. Everybody worked like a well-oiled machine and the flight ran on rails, it really did. And that's what we wanted to achieve."

Though their flight of the world's largest-ever hydrogen-electric aircraft would go on to make headlines around the world, for Killerby and Yapp, the actual experience was uneventful, which was their goal.

"As a test pilot, you don't want it to be exciting or a challenge," Killerby said, noting that all the *real* work had been done far in advance.

"The most beautiful part for me was to hug everyone when I entered the hangar and say thank you," he said. "There was not a hand I didn't shake, as everyone did something for the aircraft. If you'd taken just one of those people out, we wouldn't have achieved what we did."

For Teofili, the day was poignant because they had done every part of the tests in-house using ZeroAvia's team, something that will likely not be the case in the future as the company moves onto bigger projects, partners and aircraft.

In their initial tests, the Dornier-228 flew with two engines: the one on the left hand side was ZeroAvia's, whereas the other was a standard TPE331 Turboprop engine.[16]

Though their results have been good thus far, the team is determined to maintain focus as their test flights get longer and more challenging in preparation for commercial flight certification in 2025.

EXPANDING HYDROGEN-ELECTRIC FLIGHT FROM SIX TO 200-SEAT AIRCRAFT

In order for ZeroAvia to come to market, all of its products must be certified as safe for many different sizes of aircraft and flight ranges.

73

ZeroAvia's ZA600 powertrain is designed to power small regional aircraft with up to 19 passengers, and is planned to be the company's first commercial product, with a target date of certification in 2025.

The ZA600 will be followed by the ZA2000, which is estimated to come into service in 2026.

All of this has airlines particularly excited. This is because the ZA2000 is designed to be fitted into the workhorses of regional aviation aircraft such as the De Havilland Canada Dash 8-400, which is being flown by over 70 owners and operators worldwide.[17]

Among the interested parties is Alaska Airlines, one of ZeroAvia's investors, who delivered the company a Dash 8 on May 1, 2023 to help it run tests of its ZA2000 powertrain.[18] After that, the next major milestone comes in 2030, with the release of the ZA2000-RJ, a powertrain for regional jets.

At the June 2023 Paris Air Show, Mitsubishi Heavy Industries, which owns the CRJ family of regional jets and ZeroAVia, released a study showing that a hydrogen-electric powered CRJ aircraft could fly 60 passengers for over 1000 km. This means that 80% of regional jets flights could be powered by ZeroAvia's hydrogen-electric powertrains.[19]

ZeroAvia investor United Airlines intends to take the ZA2000-RJ powertrain and fit it into the United Express fleet of CRJ jets, of which the airline currently has over 200 in service.

But ZeroAvia's ambitions don't stop with fitting engines into regional jets serving smaller US cross-country routes. It eventually aims to break into the 100-200 seat narrowbody market.

And so in March 2023, ZeroAvia successfully tested a high temperature fuel cell unlocking "record breaking power densities," a breakthrough the company believes will eventually improve electric propulsion systems enough to power bigger, 100+ seat, single-aisle, turbofan aircraft such as the Boeing 737 and Airbus A320.[20]

Although successfully achieving all of these certifications is challenging enough, there is another piece of the puzzle Zero-Avia needs to solve: namely, the *external* logistics of partnering with countless companies and organisations to build the proper infrastructure to support these new technologies.

In simpler terms, the world's airports must be outfitted to support hydrogen-electric aircraft, which they currently aren't. Fortunately, Miftakhov's prior experience has him prepared for exactly this kind of challenge, and ZeroAvia has a plan.

THE SURPRISING EFFICIENCY OF STRATEGIC "HYDROGEN HUBS" TO SUPPORT REGIONAL FLIGHT

While it may be simple enough to retrofit older aircraft with new hydrogen-electric propulsion systems, how will this new technology actually be supported at airports around the world?

How will the new engines and powertrains be maintained and how will planes refuel?

Though some airports have started planning to add charging stations for electric and hybrid-electric aircraft, by and large, they are still only equipped to deal with fossil fuels.

Fortunately, not every airport in a given region will need to be hydrogen-enabled, particularly for airports specialising in regional flights. Instead, only a strategic number of airports will need to be converted into hydrogen hubs.

Thanks to an agreement ZeroAvia signed with hydrogen fuelling firm ZEV Station in June, the company has already scoped a scenario for 10 major airports in California to be equipped for hydrogen by 2030.[21]

In turn, those airports will be able to serve many others in the American West and Southwest, all of which will be possible by the end of the decade, when ZeroAvia's improved powertrains will enable regional jets to safely fly 1000 nautical miles.

To make infrastructure and storage even simpler, ZeroAvia intends to produce green hydrogen right at the airport using renewable energy, instead of bringing it in from the outside by tanker truck or pipeline.

ZeroAvia calls the project their Hydrogen Airport Refuelling Ecosystem (HARE), and is currently working with energy giant Shell to make their vision a reality.

The company also has a number of airport partners already onboard to help develop this ecosystem, one of which is Edmonton International Airport in Canada.

Their collaboration will involve developing hydrogen infrastructure at both the main airport and the city's secondary Villeneuve Airport, and will see ZeroAvia and Edmonton International Airport conducting a pilot programme to fuel a demonstrator aircraft before establishing some of the world's first hydrogen-electric commercial routes.[22]

ZeroAvia is also collaborating with AGS Airports (the owner of Aberdeen, Glasgow and Southampton Airports in the UK) to bring zero-emissions flights to Scotland, a logistical environment that AGS Airports CEO Derek Provan calls "the perfect test-bed" for ZeroAvia's technology.[23]

As a result of Scotland's relatively compact geography, all regional routes served from Aberdeen and Glasgow could run off of one hydrogen airport base; in turn, that one hub could also serve a number of smaller airports, namely those found in the islands and highlands of Scotland.

In deploying and scaling its hydrogen-fueling ecosystem and technology, ZeroAvia faces the unique challenge of finding airports that are neither too big nor too small to partner with. As it turns out, Scotland's Aberdeen and Glasgow airports are nearly ideal for that purpose.

As explained by Kirsten Poon, Edmonton's Director of Business Development & Investment Attraction, the airport is big enough to have international flights but small enough that any inevitable disruptions from implementing these new systems won't have excessively negative economic impacts.[24]

By contrast, significant disruptions at a major hub like

London Heathrow Airport, which connects to many other major international routes and airports, could have an enormous negative economic impact.

It's a difficult balance to strike and a tricky obstacle that Zero-Avia's flight testing department knows all too well. "Heathrow doesn't want to stop commercial traffic even for five minutes," Gabriele Teofili said.

There is also the challenge of acquainting consumers with the idea of flying in hydrogen-powered aircraft, which many consumers are still unfamiliar with.

Though today there are multiple companies looking at hydrogen-powered flights, hydrogen still has a lingering perception outside of the aviation industry, a problem dating back to the Hindenburg Airship crash of 1938.

In fact, in the early days of ZeroAvia, Miftakhov even had a picture of the Hindenburg on the second slide of his pitch deck so he could address anyone's concerns about hydrogen right away.

For Edmonton Airport's part, strategies to get passengers comfortable with the idea of hydrogen have included ordering a fleet of 100 hydrogen-electric cars from Toyota Canada, both to normalise the technology and to enable zero emissions ground transportation.

ASSEMBLING A "CITY OF AVIATION" FOR HYDROGEN-FUELED TOURISM

As Miftakhov always stresses, time is running out to decarbonise the aviation industry. Even so, the progress ZeroAvia has made with its retrofitting strategy over the past six years has given him a lot of hope.

It has also led Miftakhov to retrofit an old idiom to his own usage for the future vision of aviation. "You don't need a village to transform aviation, you need a *city*," he said. "And that city is now coming together. Everyone is aligning around this vision of clean aviation—power plants, aircraft manufacturers, airports, infrastructure players, airlines operators. But at the same time, the world has changed dramatically. The industry has changed dramatically."

To take advantage of those shifts, Miftakhov and his team at ZeroAvia are always repositioning their company to be ready for a vibrant future and making decisions they think will have positive ripple effects.

ZeroAvia's concept of hydrogen hubs is one such example which has applications far beyond streamlining airport logistics, as illustrated by ZeroAvia's emerging partnerships in the Middle East, including one with Saudi Arabia's landmark NEOM project.

In March 2023, NEOM, a 26,500 sq-km megaproject and planned smart city which will include a 170 km long, multi-story linear "city" enclosed on either side by mirrored glass (which has captured the imagination of news media around the world), announced that it would soon have its own airline.

According to CEO Klaus Goersch, it will be able to support zero-emission flights beginning in 2026. Though there hasn't been an official announcement, it doesn't take a lot of imagination to foresee that ZeroAvia-powered aircraft will be involved, given the connections between the organisations that already exist.[25]

Similarly, The Red Sea Development Company (TRSDC), another major Saudi initiative, has also started working with ZeroAvia.[26] As Middle Eastern governments and companies work to develop the coast of the Saudi Red Sea into one of the most significant new luxury tourism developments of the decade, ZeroAvia and TRSDC are looking into retrofitting a fleet of around 30 seaplane variants of the Cessna Caravan with Zero-Avia's new powertrain technology.

In the deal, TRSDC and ZeroAvia will work together to develop the technology, including collaboration on a roadmap for delivering the production, supply and infrastructure necessary to support hydrogen-powered air travel in Saudi Arabia.

Of course, all of this is just the beginning, as there are still countless other tourism authorities and luxury destinations that would make ideal candidates for ZeroAvia's approach to zero-emission flight.

Even so, at the root of Miftakhov's paradigm-shifting efforts in aviation is the more modest motivation of leaving a better world for his children, one he shares with Jon Killerby and Gabriele Teofili.

It's because of all this, as well as the efforts of aviation pioneers, that Miftakhov is looking forward to the coming decades, when more of the net-zero world he imagines will have materialised. "It's a really exciting time," Miftakhov said.

✈ KEY LESSONS FROM ZEROAVIA

1. **With an inspiring vision, you can attract experienced staff.** In this chapter, we've told stories of how experienced aviation insiders who had already achieved a lot in their careers jumped at the chance to be part of a world changing start-up. For other companies in similar situations, there's an opportunity to attract talent with essential business and technical expertise.

2. **Look for a "plug and play" approach to get to market and build an ecosystem faster.** ZeroAvia makes things easy for its airline customers: bring the aircraft in for its maintenance service, and we'll swap out the engine. As Val Miftakhov says, it's "plug and play"—an approach that increases the speed and frequency of other business deals and partnerships that inevitably follow.

3. **Exit the "Valley of Death" as soon as possible with an approach that generates cash early.** ZeroAvia has an engine model that they can sell as soon as 2025.

Rather than wait 5-10 years for revenue and have investors keep adding sums of upfront capital, the money from initial sales can be reinvested for future engine development.

4. **Build the proper infrastructure by carefully choosing the right partners.** ZeroAvia has thought about the infrastructure that will be needed for hydrogen-electric aircraft, including working with airport partners—but those partners have been carefully chosen, and include medium-sized airports like Edmonton who have scale but are also willing to innovate and experiment.

5. **Look for unlikely systemic improvements revealed by mistakes and setbacks.** Like other start-ups, ZeroAvia has had setbacks that they used as learning opportunities to improve their systems, one of which was bringing on a dedicated test pilot and strengthening their maintenance department.

6. **Remember that the largest changes require a city, not a village.** As Val Miftakhov says, it takes a city and not a village to realise the most ambitious goals—in his case, the vision of true-zero aviation. That involves bringing in as many external partners as possible, but also empowering your staff to see the important roles they play in the mission.

THREE
AIR COMPANY: FROM SCALING CARBON CAPTURE TECH WITH VODKA TO MAKING JET FUEL FROM THIN AIR

"HOW DO you take what's known as a really heavy piece of technology and science and make it palatable for people to understand?"

It was a question Gregory Constantine, CEO of Air Company, pondered on Gary Vaynerchuck's podcast *Marketing for the Now* in 2020.[1] "There are so many amazing technologies out there that don't see the light of day because the technology hasn't been able to have been met by the marketing of the business," he continued.

Though the podcast has been a home to many different tech entrepreneurs, it may still seem somewhat unusual as a place for the CEO of a jet fuel company to appear. But Air Company is not a typical company.

In Constantine's own words, Air Company's core business involves a "really heavy piece of technology." It takes captured carbon dioxide and turns it into products—beginning with vodka, perfume, and hand sanitiser.

Eventually, their experimentation culminated in the development of a revolutionary new jet fuel, one that could play a key role in helping the airline industry cut its growing share of greenhouse emissions.

As their journey shows, Constantine and Air Company's CTO Stafford "Staff" Sheehan were wary of falling into the trap of making something no one understood or heard about.

Their growth strategy combined technological innovation, a product road map that has been described as "genius," and clever marketing to build a company that has attracted heavyweight backing from the likes of NASA, the US Department of Defence, and airline JetBlue.

All this despite the fact that for the first three years of Air Company's existence, the company was mostly known as a luxury consumer goods company that made the world's first carbon negative vodka.

As they explain it, Constantine and Sheehan had a broader vision for themselves from the very beginning—but they intended to be savvy about achieving it, both by perfecting their technology and polishing their brand.

"MAKING IT" IN NEW YORK CITY BY COMBINING SCIENTIFIC INNOVATION AND MARKETING SAVVY

Despite their origins in very different industries, before they met, both Constantine and Sheehan were high flyers getting recognised for their achievements.

Originally from Australia, Constantine graduated from The University of Sydney in 2012 in Media & Communications. While at University, he combined what he learned in the classroom with practical experience, working as a marketing and tour manager for artists such as Snoop Dogg.

Upon graduating, Constantine took advantage of a year-long work visa programme between Australia and the United States. In the end, he decided to move to New York City.

"I packed my bags with no job, nothing," Constantine said, inspired by the possibility of making his own mark. "As the song goes, 'If you can make it there, you can make it anywhere.'"[2]

Upon arriving, started his life as a New Yorker in a basement apartment on Manhattan's East Side with no windows and barely any ventilation. "I was a 24-year-old who was just excited at any opportunity," he said. Fortunately, a big opportunity soon came from global beverage giant Diageo, which has a New York office.

With brands ranging from Smirnoff Vodka to Gordon's Gin, Diageo's key demographic is young adults. One of the primary ways to reach them was through live experiences and events, which lined up perfectly with Constantine's experience.

After several interviews, Diageo hired Constantine to run global festival strategy and cultural partnerships for Smirnoff.

At around the same time, Sheehan was having a very different experience. Originally from New England, he graduated from Yale with a degree in physical chemistry in 2015, amassing 10 published patents in his name.

Shortly thereafter, Sheehan co-founded Rhode Island-based Catalytic Innovations, a company which sought to reduce energy consumption in oil industry refining processes, where he also served as CEO.

Among tech, media, and entrepreneurial circles in and around New York City, the annual Forbes 30 Under 30 list is a much-anticipated list and cultural event, indicating the who's who among leaders and innovators of tomorrow.

For their respective achievements, Sheehan was included on Forbes' list in 2016 in the energy space,[3] while Constantine was featured in the marketing category in 2017.[4]

To encourage networking and creative cross-pollination, Forbes regularly organises events for its 30 under 30 cohorts. One such event was the Under 30 Summit, which took place in Israel in April 2017.[5]

Among the delegates that year were Constantine and Sheehan. After meeting and sharing drinks in Israel, the pair remained in touch and saw each other again at other networking events in and around New York. As they spent more time together, they began to consider one anothers' unique skill sets.

Included among Sheehan's patent achievements was the discovery of a new industrial material called a heterogenised homogeneous catalyst, one he thought might have application by energy companies worldwide for the production of biofuels.

Meanwhile, Constantine's experience organising high-profile events and using clear communication in partnerships appealed to Sheehan, who knew all too well how difficult it could be to translate scientific innovation into mass cultural adoption.

Over various dinners, an idea started forming in their minds: What if they combined their skills to do something no one had ever done before?

More specifically, could Constantine's marketing know-how and Sheehan's scientific expertise be combined to do something about climate change? Something technologically innovative that would make a real impact on the culture?

COMBINING ATMOSPHERIC CARBON CAPTURE AND SLEEK MARKETING BY MAKING VODKA

Since the Industrial Revolution 150 years ago, humanity has been putting an ever-increasing amount of CO_2 into the atmosphere, resulting in the climate emergency we have today.

But what's less well known is that just as we've been putting carbon dioxide into the atmosphere, we can also take it out again through a technology called carbon capture. We can then turn that captured CO_2 into everyday products such as clothes[6] or laundry detergent.[7]

In an interview with *The New York Times* in 2020, Constantine recounts the day that Sheehan presented him with "an unusual bottle of booze" made from captured CO_2. "Hold on," he said, "you made this from carbon dioxide?" Sheehan nodded.[8]

Through this revelation, Constantine and Sheehan had found a clear example to follow and a perfect way to combine their respective skills. In 2017, the pair founded Air Company, which would be dedicated to using captured carbon to make luxury products, and the first would be one Constantine knew well from his experience at Diageo: vodka.

Vodka has the advantage of being quite a simple product, as it consists of only two ingredients: ethyl alcohol and water. Typically, ethyl alcohol has been produced from fermented grains or potatoes, which has a carbon impact of up to 13 pounds per bottle due to the energy needed for transport of raw materials and during fermentation.[9]

Inspired by Sheehan's first example, the pair decided to use carbon dioxide as the basis for vodka instead of grain or potatoes. Using a process Sheehan had developed, they would mix CO_2 with hydrogen produced via renewable electricity (called green hydrogen) in a reactor, yielding the end product of ethanol.

That ethanol could then be used as the basis for vodka—and unlike every other vodka on the market, the production of this one would be carbon *negative*.

SCALING INNOVATIVE TECH AND BUILDING A BRAND WITH A HIGH-MARGIN, LUXURY PRODUCT LAUNCH STRATEGY

Although Air Company started with vodka, Sheehan and Constantine's goal was never to create a high-end beverage company.

"We'd always had large industrial markets in mind," Constantine said. After all, ethanol made from CO_2 has a wide variety of applications other than beverages. Of course, before the company could expand into new markets, their priority was to "[make] the technology work, and [make] revenue on the pathway towards scale."

An additional constraint was that their first production facility was a converted nightclub in Brooklyn, New York City, so the volume of whatever product they might produce would have to be modest. They needed something they could make at a low volume and sell at a high-margin, and vodka was the perfect answer.

Conventional fossil-fuel-based jet fuel typically costs $3-4 a gallon, while sustainable aviation jet fuel is somewhat higher, at $8-15. By contrast, a 750ml bottle of luxury vodka could be sold for $75 (the equivalent price of about $280 a gallon).

Although these products sell at different price points, the technology used to make jet fuel and vodka from CO_2 is fundamentally the same. For Air Company, this means the costs are nearly the same as well—but the profit margin for vodka is much larger.

To highlight how unique their product was, Sheehan and Constantine called it Air Vodka, adding a sign post to the fact that it was made out of thin air without emitting new greenhouse gases.

Drawing on his marketing expertise, Constantine understood that the "air" hook would have instant appeal among fashionable but climate conscious vodka drinkers in New York's bars and restaurants. It is perhaps no surprise, then, that each batch of vodka they produced sold out within hours.

After vodka, Air Company was ready to take their strategy and apply it in another area. Eventually, they settled on Air Eau de Parfum.

Like vodka, perfume is a low volume, high-end, high-price product—with the added benefit that the margins were even higher. A 50cl bottle could retail for $220, despite the fact that it involved nearly the same process, technology and costs as making vodka.

It was how Air Company made the world's first fragrance made out of thin air, once again allowing Constantine to position the company's perfume as an example of "clean beauty."[10]

For his part, Jim Lockheed of JetBlue Ventures, a current investor in Air Company, describes Constantine's and Sheehan's strategic product decisions as "genius." As he explains, Constantine and Sheehan's approach had a parallel in Tesla's Roadster.

"You make a high-margin, luxury product first," Lockheed said. "You position it well. You create scarcity. You get people interested in it. Then, you use that high margin to feed into your technology stack and into reaching economies of scale, which later on helps you produce a commodity product."

HOW AIR COMPANY'S ADAPTABLE TECH AND GOVERNMENT PARTNERSHIPS ALLOWED A POST-COVID-19 PIVOT

Before long, Constantine and Sheehan's innovative product strategy was turning heads and generating interest. Their vodka in particular got a significant amount of media attention, and was listed by *Time Magazine* as one of the best inventions of 2020.[11]

At the same time, Air Company was also getting scientific recognition, leading to the company becoming one of 10 finalists in the XPrize Carbon competition.[12]

XPrize is a non-profit organisation that hosts competitions to reward technological innovations benefitting the common good, with trustees including Google co-founder Larry Page and *Huffington Post* co-founder Arianna Huffington.

Sheehan and Constantine's introductory pitch in the competition showed exactly why they were gaining so much traction: "We know that the best solutions aren't always the most obvious, but smart executions of the right science can literally change the world."[13]

But 2020 wasn't all smooth sailing for Constantine and Sheehan. Amid a string of successes came the dawn of the COVID-19 pandemic in March 2020, turning countless industries upside down. This included the hospitality industry, which was the main buyer of the pair's vodka.

"At the time, we were focused on sales into bars and restaurants," Sheehan said. "But when COVID hit all of a sudden, that really didn't matter anymore."

Constantine and Sheehan could have waited things out and

hoped for a functioning business at the end of the pandemic. Instead, they saw another use case for their technology—one that would also help New York's overstretched hospitals.

When COVID-19 hit the US, the Food and Drug Administration (FDA) issued an emergency authorisation for distilleries to produce hand sanitiser. "Because we had extremely high purity ethanol that went beyond even pharmaceutical grade," Sheehan said, "we were able to make a really nice spray and sanitiser. We took all of the ethanol that we were going to turn into vodka and mixed it into the FDA approved mixture."

Air Company took the ethanol they'd intended to use in vodka and began to repurpose it as sanitiser, following FDA guidelines which required a composition of 80% ethanol to nominal amounts of glycerin, hydrogen peroxide and water. "We started donating these hand sanitiser bottles to hospitals in New York City and beyond," Sheehan said.

In turn, the hand sanitiser Air Company produced even attracted the attention of NASA. This came as Air Company entered NASA's CO2 conversion challenge.[14]

NASA's competition had participants convert carbon dioxide into sugars like glucose as a step to creating mission-critical resources that might be used in space flight or even on Mars.

Upon seeing Air Company's product, NASA issued a press release praising their efforts, citing the company as an example of, "change makers and problem solvers, many of whom go on to apply their technology and creativity to make a difference in their own communities and around the world."[15]

In the end, Air Company was announced as one of three winners that would share a $650,000 prize fund, though the company also received a $50,000 bonus for demonstrating "efficiency, scalability and reliability."[16]

Sheehan and Constantine's association with NASA resulted in wider credibility and recognition—though it also became critical to helping them realise their initial vision of producing products at an industrial scale.

LEVERAGING A NASA PARTNERSHIP TO BREAK FROM LUXURY CONSUMER PRODUCTS TO SUSTAINABLE AVIATION FUEL

When most people think about NASA, they likely think about space. What's less well known is that the US government agency is also very involved in helping the aviation industry tackle climate change.

Among projects that NASA is spearheading are the development of a battery that could be used in electric planes[17] and a collaboration with Boeing on the design of a new aircraft.[18] It was through its association with NASA that Air Company announced it would be researching sustainable rocket fuel.[19]

Having shown that their technology could one day even be used on Mars, Sheehan and Constantine began to dedicate themselves to exploring the project further—and in an interview with *Forbes*, Constantine offered more context.

"Organisations like SpaceX and Blue Origin have begun to look for new propellants for their rocket engines for commercial spaceflight and Mars exploration. That's where we come in. The Martian atmosphere is 95.32% CO_2 and our proprietary technology has the ability to transform that CO_2, from both the Martian atmosphere and from the air on Earth, into a fuel for a rocket engine."

Air Company has even gone as far as making food for long space missions,[20] pioneering a way to recycle the CO_2 exhaled by astronauts to grow yeast based nutrients that can be turned into protein shakes. Speaking to *Reuters*, Staff Sheehan said that "it's definitely more nutritious than Tang", and described the taste as "sweet tasting" and "almost malted."

As Air Company's vision developed, NASA wasn't the only US government agency whose support they earned. In 2021, the company was also part of Project FIERCE, a US Department of Defense initiative to test Air Company's fuel in an Unmanned Aerial Vehicle (UAV), which resulted in the first ever test flight with jet fuel made from CO_2.[21]

Since then, the links Air Company established with the US Department of Defense and NASA have only been strengthened.

RAISING $40M IN FUNDING WITH PROVEN PRODUCTS AND SCALABLE PROCESSES

Constantine and Sheehan always understood the wide range of applications for their technology, but they also knew that they would need to prove it to investors and potential customers. By 2022, having made hand sanitiser, vodka and perfume, Air Company had that proof.

Having won scientific prizes and received validation from major organisations like NASA, Air Company was soon attracting investor attention as well. In April 2022, Air Company raised $30 million in Series A Funding to be put toward scaling its technology.[22]

The round was led by Carbon Direct Capital Management, a specialist climate tech fund that has also invested in other companies working on carbon capture based technologies.[23]

Other Air Company investors included Toyota Ventures, JetBlue Technology Ventures, and Parley for the Oceans, bringing the company's total funding north of $40 million by the end of 2022.

Though it's obvious why JetBlue Ventures would be interested in low or zero carbon jet fuel, the fact still remains that there are a lot of SAF companies it could have chosen to invest in. Why did they ultimately choose Air Company?

According to Jim Lockheed, Air Company stood out by having more proof of their ability to scale than their competitors. "Most of these other companies that we had been talking to had only ever produced lab scale quantities," he said. "Everything else was kind of hypothetical. What really stood out to me about Air Company was them telling me, 'Our facility has produced something like 10,000 litres of product.'"

Sheehan and Constantine's unconventional product route

also resonated with airline Virgin Atlantic, another partner committed to buying their aviation fuel.

According to Holly Boyd-Boland, Virgin Atlantic's head of sustainability, Constantine and Sheehan's "innovator and disruptor mindset" was particularly appealing. "By producing consumer-facing products in their vodka and perfume, they are approaching carbon capture almost through a consumer lens."

THE "YIN AND YANG" OF AIR COMPANY AND THE IMPORTANCE OF INVESTING IN PEOPLE

Technological and business prowess aside, the other common reason investors have seemed to flock to Air Company is simple: they are bought into Constantine and Sheehan as people.

Though the two have had different career trajectories, they compliment each other, giving Air Company what Constantine calls a much-needed "yin and yang."

"To have a great company," Sheehan said, "you have to have both the product development and the ability to make the products. And you have to have the ability to sell not just the products but the vision, the dream, and the business."

With Constantine focusing on selling the vision and assuming the CEO role, Sheehan has been able to concentrate on making those products. "I see a lot of companies out there where the scientists don't necessarily get to focus on the science," Sheehan said, "and they haven't been as successful as we are in the technology realm."

On that point, Constantine is inspired by the wisdom of legendary Apple founder Steve Jobs. "When you merge technology and creativity," he said, "beautiful things can happen."

As Air Company shows so well, ultimately, people invest in people. For investors, completely apart from market strategy, basic chemistry and comfort with the people they invest is another crucial factor.

"You look at Greg, and you can tell he's a great leader," Lockheed said. "He's got this great background having worked at Diageo. And then you look at Staff—he's a chemist, a PhD, had the best chemistry dissertation for his year at Yale. He's got patents, he's got all these things."

For JetBlue Ventures and others, those disparate qualities are a winning combination. "They are becoming a great story and team that you look for as a venture capitalist," Lockheed said.

USING SCIENTIFIC INNOVATION TO PRODUCE A CHEAPER, FASTER AND CLEANER E-FUEL

With funding secured, Air Company officially launched its AIRMADE Sustainable Aviation Fuel at New York Climate Week in September 2022.[24]

Along with JetBlue, the company lined up Virgin Atlantic, Air Canada and supersonic aircraft company Boom as launch customers.

Sustainable Aviation Fuel, usually referred to as SAF, can be divided into two broad categories: biofuels, made from feedstock such as used cooking oil or fuel crops like acanthus, or e-fuels, made from CO_2 and renewable energy.

There are some question marks over biofuel use; for example, European NGO Transport & Environment claims that biofuels are a risk to food security, as farmland that could be used for food crops is instead being used to plant fuel crops.[25]

As such, national and international regulators are increasingly promoting the development of e-fuels. In the European Union's SAF mandate, for example, e-fuels must compose at least 2% of Europe's aviation fuel quota between 2032-2035.[26]

Unfortunately, e-fuels can also be up to seven times more expensive than conventional jet fuel, and they use an enormous amount of renewable energy to produce—so much so that Venture Capital firm World Fund came out with a knowledge paper in December 2022 claiming that even replacing 8% of Europe's aviation fuel with e-fuels by 2040 would require the equivalent electricity consumption of the Netherlands or Sweden.[27]

Air Company's AIRMADE fuel is an e-fuel, though fortunately, the company has leaned into Sheehan's innovative scientific mind to improve some of the typical production limitations.

Like all synthetic fuels, e-fuels are typically made by an almost 100-year-old chemical process called Fischer-Tropsch, which works as follows:[28]

To begin, the raw materials of hydrogen (H2) and carbon monoxide (CO) must be produced to use in the reaction. The hydrogen is made by breaking down water (H2O) in an electrolyser into hydrogen and oxygen; meanwhile, carbon monoxide is made by breaking down CO2 in a syngas generator. Once the hydrogen and carbon monoxide syngas are ready for the reaction, they are combined in what's called a Fischer-Tropsch Reactor to be turned into fuel.

This is where Sheehan's scientific innovations begin to improve on this older process.

In what has been dubbed the Sheehan Single Step Process, the need to turn CO2 into syngas is removed entirely. Instead, CO2 and H2 are combined directly in Air Company's own reactor to produce ethanol (C2H6O). According to Sheehan, this offers double the process energy efficiency of the older Fischer-Tropsch method of making synthetic fuels.[29]

In addition to being easier and more energy efficient, Air Company's AIRMADE fuel has another advantage over other SAFs. While most other SAFs result in a roughly 80% reduction in carbon emissions, Air Company's is predicted to reduce life-cycle emissions by up to 97%[30]—a key draw for airlines like JetBlue, Air Canada and Virgin Atlantic due to their net-zero targets.

Given these efficiency and sustainability benefits, Constantine is confident their product has enormous market potential. "There are close to 100 billion gallons of aviation fuel being used and consumed," he said. "Then, we have airlines with targets of the percentages of sustainable fuel that they need by 2030 and 2050—and they are not even close."

By using their fuel, however, Constantine and Sheehan believe that airlines might begin to close that gap.

PACKAGING AN ALL-IN-ONE PROCESS TO LAND A $65 MILLION USAF DEAL

Since Air Company's initial involvement in the US Defense Department's Project FIERCE, their relationship with the military has grown, culminating in February 2023 in a $65 million agreement signed with the US Air Force.

Crucially, Air Company won't be supplying the US Air Force with SAF. Instead, it will work with the USAF to produce its own fuel on site.[31]

This is part of a USAF programme called Project SynCE (pronounced "sense").[32] Again demonstrating Air Company's procedural efficiency, all stages of their SAF production will occur on-base—from carbon capture to combining raw materials in an Air Company reactor to yield jet fuel.

In addition to environmental benefits, Air Company's all-in-one process adds an obvious security benefit as well, allowing bases to be self-sufficient for their fuel.

As a caveat, the deal will result in only tens of gallons of fuel being produced. Considering that in 2017, the US Air Force bought over 250,000 barrels of oil a day, SAF will not make a big dent in the US Air Force's carbon emissions—at first.[33]

Even so, this agreement, among others the US Air Force has signed with other companies, at the very least appears to show the organisation's intent to begin shrinking their carbon emissions—which on their own are of a scale larger than many entire countries.[34]

LOOKING FOR THE "FUN" IN INDUSTRY-WIDE DISRUPTION—AND REDUCING EMISSIONS BY OVER 10%

In just a few years, Air Company took a piece of carbon capture technology, brought it to market via an unconventional business strategy, successfully pivoted when the pandemic turned many of their original markets upside down, won the support of key institutions in US government, raised funding from A-list investors, and launched a revolutionary new sustainable jet fuel.

All of this amounts to an enormous list of achievements. But Constantine and Sheehan's ambitions do not end there. In their view, if many industries around the world used Air Company's technology, global emissions could be reduced by up to 10.8% annually.[35]

Their figure comes from adding the 1.3% of global emissions from ethanol, 3.3% from methanol, and 6.1% from kerosene—all industries and fuel sources that Air Company can disrupt and decarbonise.

To help them reach that goal, Constantine and Sheehan are scoping out two "world scale production facilities" to see the company's technology applied as widely as possible. Owned and operated by Air Company, both will be live before 2030.

Though they have a clear strategy and proven processes in place, CEO Constantine is still well aware that meeting these ambitions won't be easy. "We are bullish in our confidence and the staff and team on the technical side have delivered year in, year out," he said. "The same is true on the commercial side. However, we also understand the challenges that come with scaling up any organisation that's putting steel in the ground or building hardware."

Fortunately, Constantine and Sheehan are still only in their 30s. With confidence gained from starting a world-changing company over martinis in Manhattan, the pair are ready to keep shaking things up and have the time to do it.

Constantine puts the vision simply: "We're all about changing the world and having fun while we're doing it."

1. **Mastering the "yin and yang" of commercial and scientific know-how.** Constantine and Sheehan spoke to us at length about why their different skill-sets are a winning combination. Sheehan has been able to concentrate on science and making really innovative products, but as Constantine mentions, many great technologies get nowhere when companies don't know how to market them and sell a vision. By adding those skills as CEO, the duo achieves a perfect "yin and yang" balance that maximises the success of both sides of the company.

2. **Use efficient and elegant design in both products and processes.** Air Company's vision is bold and easy to understand. It captures imaginations, and it has a clear, and consistent visual language in its branding. Its products are sleek, and its commercial and scientific processes are adaptable, allowing them to use their model to make vodka, perfume, hand sanitiser, and jet fuel. Through these elements, Air Company has internalised the importance of elegant design and efficiency in all aspects of a business. Doing so helps positioning and makes you resilient in a crisis, as shown by their smooth transition through the COVID-19 pandemic.

3. **The importance of telling a good story when investors invest in people.** Individually, Constantine and Sheehan have many impressive achievements, but together, they create an even more compelling story. On top of their technical achievements, the chemistry

created by their different viewpoints creates a magnetism that has attracted media and investors. To new founders, remember: you *do* have a good story and investors *do* want to hear it. It is your responsibility to articulate it properly.

4. **Prove your concept in an affordable, attention-capturing, and revenue-producing way.** Constantine and Sheehan began with a product that they could produce in small quantities and sell at a high price: premium vodka. Though from the outside it seemed unrelated to the larger goal of sustainable aviation, the company used it as a proof point for their technology —all while raising money and attracting attention. When they approached investors, they had something real to show, rather than just an idea.

5. **Design a business model and product that enables adaptability.** When the pandemic hit, Air Company lost the ability to sell vodka to bars and restaurants; similarly, demand for luxury lifestyle products like perfume also greatly decreased. Fortunately, their technological processes were robust and adaptable enough to be useful in pandemic circumstances as well. To pivot, they used an emergency FDA regulation to make hand sanitiser—and in keeping with their philosophy, they leveraged the crisis to gain the attention of NASA, which later helped them advance some of their more ambitious goals.

6. **Regardless of the specific approach, identify a big problem you are trying to solve.** Even when they were only making vodka, Air Company had the bigger picture in mind—namely that industry-wide, their processes and the products they might create could help decarbonise the world and lower greenhouse gas emissions by more than 10%.

7. **Innovation and disruption are different strategies, each with their own uses.** When Constantine and Sheehan talk about the effect Air Company will have on fossil-fuel-based industries, their approach is "disruptive"—namely, if their technology is widely adopted and proven as better for the world, it may replace many existing companies and processes. However, they took an "innovative" approach to improving SAF processes and to helping the USAF, which itself produces more greenhouse gas emissions than many entire countries. Innovation is a strategy of adding or subtracting to what exists, while disruption is often an aggressive and potentially destructive strategy. As such, be wary of which approach you choose to solve which problem—and look for the "fun" of collaborative innovation over aggressive destruction whenever possible.

FOUR

ARCHER AVIATION: BRINGING A FUTURISTIC VISION OF URBAN AIR MOBILITY TO THE MASSES TODAY WITH "REALISTIC INNOVATION"

AN AVIATION OUTSIDER MAKES THE JETSONS A REALITY

WHEN ADAM GOLDSTEIN, the founder and CEO of Archer Aviation, starts to describe his company's new aircraft called Midnight, he has a lot to say.

"It will be unlike any aircraft you've ever seen," he said. "Midnight will be flown by a pilot and can carry up to four passengers. It takes off and lands vertically, so it doesn't need a runway—but it also flies forward on a wing like an aeroplane, so it can fly fast at up to 150 miles per hour. And it can fly far."

As he continues, the story sounds more and more like science fiction.

"It can carry approximately a thousand pounds of payload. It can travel up to 100 miles. And it can do this while being as safe as a commercial airliner, but also up to 1000 times quieter than a helicopter. Imagine the trips that you've been taking in your car that take you 60, 90, 120 minutes sitting in traffic. Instead of that, you can now fly to your destination in five or ten minutes."

On top of all these details, Midnight will be powered by electric powertrain technology and recharged by renewable energy, so it will burn no carbon during operation. Goldstein also sees a future where there are so many of these aircraft in the skies above cities that they will work "like an air gondola, like a ski lift."

In other words, in his vision there will be a steady stream of small aircraft readily available. All customers will have to do is show up and fly.

As a final flourish, all of this will be possible for little more than the current price of an Uber or Lyft ride of the same distance.

If the association that comes to mind hearing this is *The Jetsons* and the flying car, that's by design. Anyone who browses media coverage about Archer will find a lot of references to the influential 1960s cartoon series.

Even Oscar Munoz, former United Airlines CEO and Archer board member, cites it as inspiration. "I watched the Jetsons when I was a kid," he said. "It was a cool concept."

Archer's Midnight aircraft is an eVTOL, which stands for electric vertical take off and landing; more colloquially, eVTOLs are also commonly called electric air taxis, a new approach to technology and design that many influential aviation companies are interested in.

The eVTOL space is becoming very crowded, with dozens of different players trying to bring the dream of the Jetsons to life. One report in September 2022 even put the number of eVTOL projects as high as 240 worldwide.[1]

Of course, given the cost and complexity of building a new aircraft from scratch, it is overwhelmingly likely that very few will make it through to commercial service. More specifically, some professional estimates say that the actual number of companies that will get passenger-laden eVTOLs in the air will be in the single digits.[2]

Of that small list of potential winners, there are a few names that standout. Among them are Joby, which is backed by JetBlue Ventures and Delta Airlines; Eve, which was spun out of

Brazilian aircraft manufacturer Embraer; and Boeing's eVTOL subsidiary Wisk.[3]

At the front of the pack is also Archer Aviation, which has now raised more than $1 billion, including from car giant Stellantis and from United, one of the world's biggest airlines. In all, Archer's recipe for success depends on two key elements, the first of which is Goldstein's confident and idea-driven leadership.

Goldstein's favourite film is *Interstellar*, where a group of astronauts travel to find a new home for humanity as Earth becomes increasingly uninhabitable—a fitting choice for a man who loves sci-fi for its approach to big problems and how we might solve them.

Of course, Goldstein also knows that many big ideas never make it out of our imagination, because nobody figures out how to make them happen.

"Archer isn't a science project," Goldstein said, stressing that this impending vision of the future is going to become very real.

All of this leads to the second crucial element driving Archer's success: a company culture of "realistic innovation," the concept of innovating only where it truly matters, and using existing technology everywhere else.

In an industry that encourages unfettered innovation and big dreams, this combination of traits helps Archer stand out. The company's vision of the future begins with technology that is available *today*. They are not waiting for some far-off change to innovation to start bringing it into the now.

And that difference in the company's DNA may stem from Adam Goldstein, who came to aviation as an outsider.

ARCHER'S FOUR PILLARS OF SUCCESS: FUNDING, DESIGN, MARKETING, AND MODELLING

Archer Aviation was founded in October 2018. Though the company is now headquartered in San Clara, California, in the first two years of its existence, its initial base was in Gainesville, at the University of Florida, which is where Goldstein received his degree in Business Administration.

After graduating, Goldstein worked in corporate finance and in the start-up world, but not in aviation.

However, the emerging field of Urban Air Mobility (UAM), using small electric aircraft to serve commuter routes in metropolitan areas, caught his attention, leading to the creation of Archer Aviation.

Though there were some raised eyebrows at his lack of aviation expertise, Goldstein says that the work he did previously as an entrepreneur served as invaluable experience and perfect preparation for Archer.

"What's really important is the ability to build and scale a company," he said. "You need to be able to raise enough capital to accomplish something that's very, very hard. And you need to know when it's time to stop doing R&D projects and to start commercialising."

Despite whatever scepticism might have come from industry insiders, blue chip investment bank JP Morgan certainly hasn't seen the lack of prior aviation experience as a hindrance.

In an April 28, 2022 investors' note, research analysts Mahima Kakani and Bill Peterson gave Archer a ringing endorsement, predicting that the company would soar in what they expected to become a $1 trillion eVTOL market.[4] According to Kakani and Peterson, Archer had a robust balance sheet—and if anything, its shares were undervalued.

JP Morgan also praised Archer for its engine design and partnerships inked with Stellantis and United Airlines. Several months later, in August 2022, Archer's stock price soared by 20% after a stock analyst at Raymond James gave the company an "outperform" rating.

Golstein articulated his leadership principles, and the reasons why Archer is so far ahead of most of the eVTOL pack at Archer's November 2022 Open House Day.

As he explained, many of Archer's competitors "started with the technology" and wanted to build a flashy, high-performance vehicle for its own sake. By contrast, Archer decided to begin with the business case and let the technology follow.

As Goldstein outlined, this laser focus on business applications is why Archer, unlike most of its competitors, is well on the way to commercial flight in 2025.[5] All of that success relied on building four pillars of the business: funding, design, marketing, and modelling.

In order: Archer has all the funding it needs to see it through to commercial flight in 2025; their design has been optimised for performance and an amazing passenger experience; the company's data has led it towards concentrating on major urban markets; and their business model has been built with data the same way.

Of course, to see the vision more clearly, it helps to see how Archer built through each of these stages one at a time.

THE "MISSION CRITICAL" TASK OF RAISING $1B IN STARTUP CAPITAL

In May 2020, *Forbes* ran a largely positive piece about Archer, though it led with the headline "Archer buys its way into the electric air taxi race."[6]

For however backhanded a compliment it may have been, it had no effect on Goldstein or the rest of Archer's leadership. In their view, raising capital couldn't be seen as anything other than a good thing. Doing so was absolutely mission critical.

"Probably the best filter that knocks out most of these companies [in the eVTOL space] is capital," Goldstein said. "It takes a lot of money to get through the certification process."

As Goldstein explains, building a completely new aircraft means hiring a team with the necessary skills, working on designs, producing aircraft, and testing them before finally trying for certification. The process takes at least five years, usually more—and during that time, aviation companies are typically burning through cash without any certified product to sell or operate.

Doing all of these things, Goldstein says, requires at least $500 million, though a more realistic figure would be closer to $1 billion.

Given how difficult this challenge is, and the fact that thousands of start-ups are looking for funding from the VC community, how does an upstart aviation company even begin to tackle this process? And if they manage to get any attention, how do they cut through?

One way is to capture the interest of a big name investor willing to take a big risk, which can lend a company credibility, business expertise and access to a broader network of connections and capital. It was the strategy that led Archer to Marc Lore.

Lore is best known for co-founding online retailer Jet.com before selling it to Walmart for $3.3 billion, after which Lore became CEO of Walmart's online arm.[7] Though Lore normally didn't invest in things outside of his close friends and family, he decided to make an exception as he was a believer in the power of electric air taxis to change the world.[8]

Lore managed to open many doors for Archer while still using his close knit approach to fundraising and investing. "Marc has raised a lot of capital from family offices and wealthy people with an interest in tech," Goldstein said—among them actress and singer Jennifer Lopez and baseball player Alex Rodriguez.[9]

In total, Lore helped engineer a Series A round for Archer in July 2020 which resulted in $55.7 million in fundraising.[10] It was an excellent start, but as Goldstein knew, it wasn't going to be nearly enough.

To raise the rest of the funds they needed, the company listed on the New York Stock Exchange (NYSE) in February 2021 via an investment vehicle called a SPAC, a Special Purpose Acquisition Company.

More specifically, a SPAC is a shell company that raises money through an Initial Public Offering (IPO) with the goal of acquiring a private company, thus offering a faster and more streamlined path for a company to go public. Doing so can provide companies with access to a wider pool of capital than they would otherwise have.

While SPACs have been around for decades, their popularity soared between 2020 and 2021, coinciding with the soaring bull market that coincided with the COVID-19 pandemic.

Archer's chosen SPAC was the Atlas Crest Investment Corp, whose shareholders ended up acquiring Archer in a kind of reverse merger.

Archer then started trading under the ticker symbol ACHR.[11]

The move made headlines in early 2021, but it wasn't the only reason Archer was in the news. Around the same time, it also netted its first major customer in United Airlines. Under the terms of an initial agreement, the airline has ordered $1 billion of Archer's aircraft, with an option to purchase more to the value of $500 million.[12]

United also committed to helping Archer solve other complex logistics problems like air traffic management. Former United Airlines CEO Oscar Munoz joined Archer's board, bringing with him decades of business expertise, while United itself invested $25 million as part of the SPAC transaction.

Thereafter, Archer revealed it had another big backer in Fiat Chrysler Automobiles (FCA), with an initial agreement involving FCA's commitment to help the startup with production, supply chain management, and design on a cockpit for their aircraft.[13] FCA is now part of car giant Stellantis.

By the time it was successfully listed on the NYSE, Archer was valued at $1.7 billion. In its investor presentation,[14] the company said its goal would be to produce 2300 aircraft and achieve a revenue of over $12 billion by the year 2030.

With funding in place, the stage was set to move onto design.

LEVERAGING STRATEGIC RECRUITING EXPERIENCE TO ASSEMBLE A PRODUCT DESIGN SUPERTEAM

While Goldstein didn't have any aircraft design expertise, he knew some of the talent that they needed could be found at his alma mater, the University of Florida.

Around the same time Archer was founded in 2018, a team working with the University of Florida's Dr. Peter Ifju was successfully building an unmanned electric hydrofoil. In Dr. Ifju and his team, Archer had a perfect potential talent pool that they could draw upon.

In a 2021 interview, Dr. Ifju recounted how his department received funding from Archer, along with a stipulation to come up with a fully functional small prototype of an eVTOL.[15]

"By December 2018, our team had built a model that was 42 inches long by 42 inches wide and weighed about 15-20 pounds," Dr. Ifju said. "We flight-tested it for them in late December 2018, and they were quite pleased with the results."

Archer was so pleased in fact, that the company continued funding Dr. Ifju's team, who by April 2019 had developed a full scale mockup of an eVTOL that was 20 feet long and 20 feet wide, weighing 1600 lb.

According to Dr. Ifju, this early prototype "had GPS, inertial measurement units, accelerometers, gyros, air speed sensors, altimeters and more—basically all the technology we employ in drones, now housed in the larger footprint of our eVTOL."

With its electric air taxi design starting to take shape, Archer was ready to scale and moved its headquarters to California, and the work done by the University of Florida team was carried on by Archer's own staff. Even so, the company's links to the University of Florida have still remained strong since.

In November 2021, the doors opened on an Archer eVTOL lab, both to help Archer with future UAM research and to give University of Florida engineering students important hands-on experience working on real world projects.[16]

Even the name Archer is a nod to the important role the University of Florida played in the development of the company, as Dr. Ifju's lab in Gainesville, Florida happens to be located on Archer Road.

Though the name was used informally at first, after later marketing research saw that it resonated with consumers, Archer decided to stick with it.

After its initial fundraising round, the company hired top rank talent. This includes Tom Muniz, who is now Archer's COO. Muniz's involvement in electric air taxis started with Zee. Aero, an early prototype backed by Google founder Larry Page.

Muniz subsequently became head of engineering at Wisk, an eVTOL company started by Larry Page's Kitty Hawk corporation and Boeing. They also brought on Geoff Bower, another Zee. Aero alumni who had also been the chief engineer on the now-shuttered Airbus Vahana eVTOL prototype project.[17]

This team was instrumental in building and then unveiling Archer's demonstrator aircraft called Maker, a two-seated eVTOL that could travel for 60 miles at a top speed of 150 mph, in June 2021.[18] At the same time, as test flights were being done on Maker, work was going into developing its production aircraft, Midnight, with the first craft built for pre-certification testing in May 2023.[19]

In the design of Midnight, one crucial area that Archer wanted to focus their innovative efforts on was the flying experience itself. More specifically, the team wanted Midnight to have an aura of magic about it.

"Since the advent of the aeroplane, aircraft have always been about utility," Goldstein said. "But we didn't want to just build a product that was about utility. We wanted to design and build our aircraft to combine high function with high emotion."

As such, the design of the aircraft is striking with two fixed wings, each with six engines, and a distinctive black shell with large windows.

Key to Midnight's design and the *wow* factor the team

wanted was Julien Montousse, Archer's head of design and innovation and former senior director of design at carmaker Mazda.

According to Mountousse, the underlying design philosophy behind Midnight was simple. "We wanted to inspire people," he said. "To make air travel feel more personal."

To do so, Mountousse and his team drew inspiration from the golden age of flying in the 1950s, getting in the headspace of passengers from that era. "It was a big experience in life," Mountousse said. "It led to real fascination with the aircraft themselves, and we wanted to bring that magical feeling back."

To do that required giving their product a very distinct identity. The aim was for it to look confident; he wanted Archer's Midnight to be identifiable from a distance. As such, Midnight was designed to have a unique vertical light on the nose of the plane—"Archer's first brand DNA signature," according to Mountousse.

To make the first moments of the cabin experience feel smooth and distinctive, the team put partial divides in between the seats to display each passenger's personal trip information. Upon boarding the aircraft, each passenger will see their name assigned to their seat, along with their destination and take off time.

Since Archer offers sustainable, all-electric flight, Mountousse stressed the importance of integrating renewable materials into the cabin design, each one telling its own unique story. Flax fibre was chosen to make the seats, while the fabric will be made out of recycled bottles.

Unlike the porthole style windows in many other aircraft, Archer's Midnight will have panoramic glass windows to allow passengers to "fully [engage] with the city below." Although the glass adds weight to the aircraft, it remained an important enough detail to the passenger experience for Archer to prioritise.

Finally, the company also wanted to make the onboarding

and offboarding experience hands-free. To make that happen, the landing gear was adapted to allow the aircraft to sit lower to the ground.

The result is that the final cabin will have the height of a midsize SUV, making it easy to get in and out of with a small bag, phone and a cup of coffee in hand.

According to Mountousse, the end result of Midnight is what happens when design and engineering excellence combine.

USING PROPRIETARY DATA TO ELIMINATE DOUBT WHEN IDENTIFYING A TARGET MARKET

Though Archer's design team put a lot of time into the experience passengers will have on Midnight, the passengers themselves likely won't spend much time absorbing it.

That's because Archer's core market is urban journeys of around 20 miles, despite the fact that Midnight has a range of about 100 miles.

Even so, the 20 mile figure was chosen very carefully. "We looked at where people are travelling on the ground, today," Goldstein said. It was an important part of the company's data-driven marketing plan, driven in part by a proprietary data tool called Prime Radiant.

Powered by large-scale optimisation and machine learning models, Prime Radiant allowed Archer to better understand how people travel within cities around the world. The project was headed by Jon Petersen, Archer's VP of Data Science, who joined the company from Uber.

Through data modelling, Petersen and his team guide decisions related to Archer's vehicle specification requirements for speed, range, and passenger capacity, as well as for a host of logistical problems including passenger pooling, aircraft routing, and battery charging.

After analysing that information, Archer estimates the overall market size and revenue opportunity in a particular city.

From looking at the data, Goldstein says Archer has been able to create very sophisticated pictures of urban environments. "There are millions and millions of people on an everyday basis who are willing to spend 60 or 90 minutes in a car on a very short trip," he said, particularly in Los Angeles. "More than five million people a day spend more than an hour in a car, going 20 miles or less."

In line with Archer's analysis, studies have shown that In Chicago, commuters lost the equivalent of four days sitting in traffic in 2021.[20] In New York, 30 million people per year travel from the city to one its three airports—Newark, JFK, and La Guardia—by car. That journey can take up to an hour and a half sitting in traffic.

It's why major US cities like New York and Chicago are where Midnight will make its first public appearances, beginning with flights from city centres to airports.

With United Airlines as the first launch customer, Archer plans to partner with the airline to transfer passengers from Manhattan to United's Newark hub,[21] as well as from downtown Chicago to Chicago's O'Hare Airport, another key United hub.[22]

These developments are especially exciting to Former United CEO and Archer board member Oscar Munoz, who is a Chicago resident himself. "I live 19 miles from the airport," he said. "It could take me 40 minutes, or it could take me three hours. Now, we'll be able to fly from downtown Chicago to O'Hare in under 10 minutes."

According to Munoz, it's a time-saving possibility that will soon be open to a lot of different people all around the world.

Right now, helicopters can already transfer a small number of passengers from helipads in city centres to airports, but their use is heavily restricted because of noise; communities are understandably reluctant to have the sound of helicopters overhead at all hours of day and night.

By comparison Midnight is sustainable both in terms of emissions and noise pollution; its batteries are recharged by renewable energy and its flights will be almost 1000 times quieter than a helicopter.[23]

That low noise footprint means Archer can drastically increase the number of places it can take off and land from, far beyond the existing heliport infrastructure. Even so, the company faces the additional challenge of needing to build its own infrastructure to support these points of departure.

In order to do so, Archer has partnered with REEF, the largest operator of mobility and logistics hubs in the US, to start identifying areas for their so-called vertiports in major US cities.[24] With a vertiport network in place, Archer will be able to branch out and serve commuter routes in major cities.

Archer's ultimate vision is to "[democratise] the skies," and Goldstein wants to eventually make flights on Midnight comparable to the rideshare prices of Uber and Lyft.[25] Of course, Goldstein recognises that this can only be achieved once Midnight is being produced at scale.

WHY THE OLYMPICS WILL MAKE 2028 A WATERSHED YEAR FOR EVTOLS

When it comes to drastically lowering their flight prices, Goldstein breaks down Archer's business model, and how it fits into the eVTOL industry, in three distinct phases.

The first phase is all about getting to market, which is where Archer is right now. The second is the commercial launch in 2025 to around 2028. Goldstein says that during this time, there will be "multiple routes in one city, and then multiple routes in multiple cities."

In many ways, 2028 will be the year of opportunity for the eVTOL industry, as it's also the year of the 2028 Olympics in LA. As a global television event, the Olympics will draw billions of eyes worldwide—and the FAA is already aspiring to have eVTOLs certified and flying before then to enable electric air taxi routes for spectators and athletes.[26]

It means that in 2028, billions of people worldwide will see what looks like flying cars from *The Jetsons* soaring over the skies of Southern California on their TV screens. By then, Goldstein believes that Archer and other eVTOL companies will have proven out the benefits, need, and demand for their aircraft. That's the third phase, when eVTOLs will start to have mass appeal.

But even then, according to Goldstein, eVTOLs will still be nowhere near realising their potential. After all, there will still be far fewer eVTOLs than helicopters. "When you step back and think about it, there are around 50,000 helicopters today," he said. "By the end of the decade, there will be less than 6000 of our planes. So we're not even denting the market."

In other words, eVTOLs still have incredible growth potential in the next decade—but people might not see it coming at first. "We'll start small," Goldstein said. "We'll start in cities. And we'll grow that over time."

WILL EVTOLS MAKE MILITARY HELICOPTERS OBSOLETE?

eVTOL makers like Archer don't only have the potential to disrupt urban transport. The US military is looking at how electric air taxis such as Midnight might be able to replace helicopters.

Archer has been working with the US Air Force since 2021, when it agreed to provide the USAF with data from selected flight tests for the purposes of furthering the USAF's understanding of its aircraft's capabilities, systems and development progression.[27]

This relationship was taken much further when at the end of July 2023, Archer and the US Air Force entered into contracts worth $142 million[28] that will see Archer initially deliver the USAF six Midnight aircraft.[29]

Following on from the USAF announcement, in August 2023, Archer was visited by the US Marine Corps to assess how the

Midnight aircraft could be integrated into personnel transport, logistics and rescue missions.[30]

All this led the military trade journal Military & Aerospace Electronics to question whether these deals could "ground choppers."[31] According to the publication, the low noise profile of eVTOLs, the fact that they are electrically powered (meaning fuel doesn't have to be transported for their use) and the target 1000 lb payload, "represents a potential paradigm shift in military aviation and operations."

This comes as Archer formed a Government Services Advisory Board in May 2023 to help the company engage more with US Government agencies and departments.[32] This board includes retired two and three star generals, who will lend Archer their expertise of having served in leadership positions within the US military.

RECRUITING TECHNOLOGICAL PARTNERS TO HELP BUILD THE FUTURE OF AVIATION

However, before Archer's aircraft are used by the military and consumers, the technology behind Midnight needs to be perfected, and it needs to be certified.

A key member of the Archer team responsible for making that happen is Dr. Michael Schwekutsch.

During his tenure at electric car manufacturer Tesla, Dr. Schwekutsch ran the powertrain team and gained invaluable experience working on electric batteries. After that, he worked for Apple in Special Projects, which is reportedly working on technology for self-driving cars.[33]

Today, Dr. Schwekutsch is Archer's senior vice president of engineering, where he's brought with him a number of lessons from Silicon Valley, especially what companies there get both right and wrong.

"When you're looking at Silicon Valley, there is a lot of leading edge, next generation, innovation," said Dr.

Schwekutsch. "Everything is questioned, everything is turned upside down, and we develop a lot of stuff." Even so, Dr. Schwekutsch has identified two areas where companies struggle.

Firstly, Silicon Valley companies often don't get a product 100% right before the official release date, and will instead iron out any remaining issues post-launch. A prime illustration of this model is the smartphone. "Just remember your last smartphone," he said. "How long did it take before you got a software update? A week? Two weeks?"

While this method might be okay in consumer electronics, in aviation, it isn't. "For one, it would be the wrong thing to do," Dr. Schwekutsch said, "and two, obviously the FAA won't let you launch the product if you say, 'Well, we'll fix it in the field later on.'"

Like any responsible aviation company, safety is a critical concern for the Archer team. "The aeroplane needs to be safe," Dr. Schwekutsch said. "There is no other way to do it. I want to fly in it. I want my family to fly in it. So we can't cut any corners."

Another issue many Silicon Valley companies have is that they try to do everything themselves. By contrast, taking such an approach in aviation would be—and often is—exorbitantly expensive. It was out of this concern, in particular, that Archer developed its own "realistic innovation" approach.

"We focus our innovation on the stuff that makes a difference," Dr. Schwekutsch said. "A difference for our customer, and a difference for the product."

As an example, Dr. Schwekutsch turned to aircraft tyres, which Archer had no interest in developing on its own. "We don't think there is a point in developing new tyres for an eVTOL aircraft," he said. "There are other companies out there. We have world-class suppliers that can help us in many, many areas that support us. Why would we go and try to reinvent the wheel, in this case, just for the sake of reinventing the wheel?"

On the other hand, the electric powertrain that feeds energy to the propellers is obviously crucial to Midnight's performance. As such, Dr. Schwekutsch and his team dedicated extra effort there, knowing it would truly matter.

The company is sourcing its batteries from Taiwanese company Molicel, an established battery maker.[34] Each plane requires six battery packs, with each pack supporting two motors at a time. These battery packs are all connected to each other, which allows them to intelligently shuttle energy back and forth.

The system architecture is unique to Archer, and has resulted in a comparatively more efficient design, with a 20% reduction in power requirements. Since battery weight is a major issue that can limit the range of electric aircraft, that 20% is really significant.

A battery pack on one of Archer's Midnight aircraft will be good for over 10,000 missions of 20 miles before needing to be replaced; meanwhile, the time it will take to charge for a 20-minute flight will only require ten minutes, allowing for rapid turnarounds in urban centres.

All of this covers the specifications of the engine and the aircraft, but how will it be manufactured?

In January 2023, Goldstein and Stellantis CEO Carlos Tavares held a joint interview on CNBC. In that interview, they announced that Stellantis would be providing the manufacturing "muscle" for Archer's Midnight aircraft.[35]

In the interview, Tavares pointed out Stellantis's impressive production specs. As the company makes more than half a million cars a month with more than 4000 parts per car, Stellantis has the experience necessary to help make Archer's vision of producing Midnight aircraft at scale a reality.

Stellantis additionally committed to provide up to $150 million in equity capital for potential draw by Archer, subject to the achievement of certain business milestones, and emphasised that this was part of Stellantis becoming "a long-term, corner-stone investor in Archer."[36]

With Stellantis's help, Archer's Midnight aircraft will be built in Covington, Georgia in a 350,000 square foot facility.[37] Initially, the facility will produce 650 aircraft a year, though the aim is to add an additional 800,000 square feet to the facility, enabling it to produce 2300 per year.

HIRING DIRECTLY FROM THE FAA AND KEEPING REGULATION IN MIND FROM THE START

Just as Archer has applied its realistic innovation ideas to all other parts of its process, none of it would matter if the regulators, in this case the FAA in the United States, were unwilling to certify that Midnight is safe and give it the green light to fly.

To account for that, Archer has hired senior executives from the FAA, who have first hand knowledge about the certification process. This includes Dr. Michael Romanowski as their head of government relations. Dr. Romanowski's previous role at the FAA included liaising with representatives from Archer—and during that time, Dr. Romanowski was impressed at Archer's dedication and focus on certification right from the start.

In June 2023, Archer then brought on former FAA administrator Billy Nolen as the company's Chief Safety Officer.[38] While at the FAA, Nolen led the agency's efforts to enable the safe entry of eVTOL aircraft into US skies.

Archer COO Tom Muniz says that involving the FAA throughout the whole process has also avoided running into surprises that would've cost the company time and money down the line, as even seemingly small changes to the aircraft can have a big impact on the business.

Imagine, for example, that the FAA review required 10% of the aircraft to be altered. Though that sounds slight, in aviation, it is enormous. "In aviation, everything is connected," Muniz said. "You can't just change one thing and expect everything else to stay the same."

In reality, 10% can sometimes mean redesigning an entire aircraft.

Romanowski, who is now dealing with his former colleagues at the FAA, is more than confident that the certification process will be successful; he actually believes that Midnight will set new standards entirely.

"I believe these vehicles are going to markedly [raise] the bar on safety," Dr. Romanowski said—particularly because of the redundancies, simplified operations, and lower maintenance costs built into them.

A BUSINESS MODEL AND STRATEGIC TEAM ROBUST ENOUGH TO WITHSTAND SHOCKS

The 19th century Prussian General Moltke is famous for saying, "No plan survives contact with the enemy." His insight applies in business, where it is nearly inevitable to run into crises and surprises that test a product's roadmap or a business plan.

But even with some inevitable bumps in the road, Archer has proven its resilience again and again.

One example is a potentially lengthy and costly legal battle that Archer faced with Wisk, the Boeing-baked eVTOL maker. This followed Archer persuading Tom Muniz, Wisk's former head of engineering, to join the company, along with a number of his colleagues.

Wisk suspected foul play and in 2021 sued Archer for alleged theft of trade secrets.[39] Archer counter-sued, stating that Wisk's allegations were a "false and malicious extrajudicial smear campaign" that impacted its business relationships and ability to raise capital.[40]

However, not only did this case reach an amicable conclusion, in August 2023 Wisk owner Boeing even ended up joining as another big name investor in Archer.

In what tech industry publication *TechCrunch* called "a somewhat surprise twist", Archer agreed to make Wisk its sole provider of autonomous flight technology.[41]

Unlike the other major eVTOL companies, Wisk's business model is to fly autonomously without a pilot, and this now opens up the prospect of Archer similarly developing a pilotless aircraft in the future.

At the same time, Boeing took part in a $215 million fundraising round, at which United Airlines and Stellantis also participated, while Wisk has the option of purchasing further shares in Archer.

The way a potential crisis like this has been overcome shows that Goldstein has kept steering a steady ship, and the underlying foundations of Archer remain strong.

A SIMPLE MANTRA TO ACHIEVE THE IMPOSSIBLE: "FOLLOW THE DATA, FOLLOW THE RESEARCH"

In spite of his lack of prior aviation experience, Goldstein reflects on Archer's success by mentioning some advice from a former boss: "Follow the research wherever it takes you. If you can trust the data, and you truly follow the research, it can show you amazing things."

According to Goldstein, that was invaluable advice. "I applied a lot of that to thinking about eVTOLs," he said. "When I thought about this industry, I saw that the technology had really evolved, that the batteries were there where we could build a product and the regulatory environment was set up."

Archer's philosophy of trusting hard evidence, innovating where it matters, being laser focused on the business case, and building the relationships with the right team and partners is why if you are in a major US city in 2025, part of your journey could well be via Archer's Midnight aircraft—even if to many, it still sounds like something from *The Jetsons*.

"It sounded crazy because it was nicknamed flying cars, but

it wasn't crazy," Goldstein said. "It was super doable. 'Follow the data, follow the research.'"

✈ KEY LESSONS FROM ARCHER AVIATION

1. **Embrace realistic innovation and don't reinvent the wheel.** Where as a startup can you employ your resources most effectively? And where can you bring on partners and use their existing experience? We've seen Archer follow this philosophy successfully throughout this chapter.

2. **Find an A-list backer to establish credibility and open doors.** There are thousands of startups vying for VC attention and funding. Having one big name on board can help make the fund raising process much smoother, as well as giving you invaluable business advice.

3. **Hire strategically to fill the gaps in your expertise.** As a founder, you don't need to know everything. But you need to bring on proven experts who know what you don't know, and you need to empower them to do their jobs well.

4. **Use data and research to identify your market.** Archer hasn't taken an educated guess on where it should initially base its aircraft. It has a proprietary data tool that tells the potential of each market.

5. **Don't focus entirely on utility—weave some magic into your product.** Archer's Midnight aircraft has that all-important *wow* factor. It will be distinctive, recognisable, it has a clear brand DNA. This is a completely new kind of aircraft, passengers need to feel and sense that it is different to anything they have flown before.

6. **Bring on experienced partners to help with commercialisation.** Archer's two main backers are United Airlines and Stellantis. Stellantis provides Archer with manufacturing muscle, and Archer's first flights will involve taking United customers to the airline's hub airports. Both partners have played a key role in helping Archer fly commercially.

7. **Work with regulators from the very start.** The regulator can make or break your whole business. Involve them at every stage of the design and production process, to avoid any unpleasant surprises further on down the line.

PART THREE
THE INSIDE JOB

FIVE

EMBRAER'S ROAD TO NET ZERO: "THE MISSION DEFINES THE ARCHITECTURE"

HOW EVE AIR MOBILITY WANTS TO CHANGE HOW PEOPLE TRAVEL

IN THE 1930S AND 1940S, the Douglas DC-3 plane revolutionised commercial air travel, making it more accessible to the average consumer thanks to a combination of high speed, low operating costs, and a comfortable passenger cabin.

Such watershed moments are relatively rare in any industry, particularly in industries with extremely high costs of entry like aviation. All the same, Andre Stein, the Chief Strategy Officer of Eve, is currently at work on an aircraft that he says will be as transformative as the DC-3 was in the '30s.

But rather than transform the way people cross continents, Eve will transform the way people travel across shorter distances (and across cities in particular).

"Think about everything that aviation has done for transportation," Stein said. "Today, you can cross an ocean in just a few hours—but then it may take a few hours more just to cross the city. Our idea is to bring that kind of mobility closer to people in the city."

The aircraft Eve is developing is an eVTOL, an Electric Take-Off and Landing aircraft, meaning it can take off vertically like a helicopter but fly horizontally like a plane. And it is fully battery-powered, with batteries recharged by renewable energy, leaving no carbon footprint.

Since eVTOLs are low-noise, flying them in cities won't be disruptive to local residents. As Stein explains, in a city like Miami, a standing fleet of 200 of his aircraft could serve "almost 100 different routes from 30 vertiports," making travel across the city at busy times exponentially faster.

Scheduled to come into service in 2026, Eve will initially carry four passengers and a pilot, but the eventual vision is to remove the cockpit and have the aircraft fly autonomously with a capacity for six passengers.

Eve is one of a large number of companies in the very crowded eVTOL space, with a report from September 2022 estimating that there are as many as 240 fledgling eVTOL companies worldwide.[1] Given that developing a new aircraft can easily cost $1 billion, it's likely that only a single-digit number of those 240 will make it through to commercial service.

Among other forerunners like Archer and Joby,[2] Eve is almost certain to be among the few who make it through. This is partly because of what Stein calls Eve's "secret sauce," namely its unique financial and cultural origins which have given it "the agility and focus of a startup with the background of an aerospace leader."

That's because although Eve is an independent company, it was spun out of Brazilian aerospace leader and manufacturer Embraer, the world's third largest commercial aircraft maker after Airbus and Boeing, who still maintain a controlling interest as the majority shareholder.

THE AGILITY OF A STARTUP WITH THE ABILITY OF A GIANT

Unlike Airbus and Boeing, Embraer doesn't make widebody aircraft. Instead, it specialises in private jets, regional aircraft and narrowbodies, from their 10-seat Phenom 100 business jet to the

Embraer E195 E2, which can carry 146 passengers in a single class or 122 passengers in a two class configuration.

Embraer has a 50+ year track record of designing, building and certifying over 30 different kinds of aircraft in precisely this segment, giving it a key competitive advantage. It understands the market, it has a global customer base and it knows how to build and launch new aircraft.

This background is particularly beneficial in the eVTOL race, because for at least the next two decades, zero emissions technologies are likely to be deployed exclusively in smaller aircraft with 100 seats or fewer.

According to Stein, being part of the Embraer family also means Eve can draw on institutional expertise as needed. "We need different expertise throughout the process," Stein said, "particularly during the development of any aircraft. At times, you're going to need an expert in a certain area. We have direct access to that without [needing to hire] someone just for a couple of weeks."

Beyond simply providing support, Eve's connection to Embraer provides them almost countless opportunities to cut costs and find synergy. "We can have access to all the background IP from Embraer royalty free," he said, "and we're outsourcing a lot of the development to the Embraer engineers."

It also allows Eve access to Embraer's own production facilities in Brazil, the United States and Portugal—and as Stein said to "the largest test facility in the Southern Hemisphere."

The connection is so close that Luis Carlos Affonso, Embraer's Senior Vice President of Engineering and Technology Development, is also Eve's chairman.

EMBRAER'S MANTRA: "THE MISSION DEFINES THE ARCHITECTURE"

Embraer has a wide net-zero strategy which rests on four different technologies, of which Eve's fully battery electric eVTOLs are just one part. Following their introduction in 2026,

Embraer plans to introduce a completely new family of regional aircraft they call Energia as well, the first of which will be hybrid-electric.[3]

These vehicles will combine an electric battery with a standard kerosene-powered turbine engine, though according to Embraer, once these Energia aircraft are adapted to use Sustainable Aviation Fuel (SAF), the entire line's emissions will be reduced by 90%. The company expects to launch both a 19 and 30-seat variant of these hybrid-electric planes early in the next decade. These will be followed by the next generation of Energia aircraft with the same seat arrangements around 2035, though these will come equipped with hydrogen fuel cells and will have no greenhouse gas emissions whatsoever.

Eve's eVTOL and the Eve and Energia aircraft families are launching for the urban and short regional markets, respectively. For longer regional routes and bigger aircraft, Embraer also intends to overhaul the E195, its largest aircraft, to become 100% certified to fly with SAF within the decade (though the timeline is subject to getting all necessary approvals from regulators).

Embraer's bets on multiple approaches set it apart from fellow aerospace giants Airbus and Boeing; Airbus is placing a big bet on hydrogen and intends to develop a 100-200 seat narrowbody by the mid-2030s, whereas Boeing believes that with 20,000+ commercial aircraft in the sky today—a number that is likely to increase to more than 40,000 by 2050—the biggest emphasis should be on SAF.

Of course, working on smaller aircraft in the Eve and Energia families will allow Embraer a stepping stone approach to developing and refining new technologies. "This will enable the scaling up and infusion of lower or zero carbon architectures on bigger aircraft in the future while still delivering a viable solution for the shorter haul flights of today," Affonso said.

Above all, Affonso says Embraer's diverse approach is deliberate. "We like to say that the mission defines the architecture. There is no one, single solution for all different sizes of aircraft."

EVE TAKES A LEADING ROLE IN THE DEVELOPMENT OF ELECTRIC URBAN AIR MOBILITY

At Eve, the mission is advanced air mobility, transporting small numbers of people short distances but at high frequency—and the architecture is a fully battery electric aircraft that doesn't need an airport to land.

As Stein says, the electric approach is a perfect fit for Eve's mission. It even allows the company to think more broadly about what an aircraft should be.

"Aeroplanes, as amazing as they are, have converged to a tube and a wing in the last half century," Stein said, "which is the best potential design to carry people with turbines." Of course, there's no rule that an aircraft *must* follow that turbine-based model.

"Electrification gives you basically a blank canvas when it comes to design," Stein said. "Electrification gives you freedom. Electrical motors are much smaller, lighter and simpler than turbines or internal combustion engines. With that, you can have things like distributed propulsion and more small motors around the aircraft."

With that diversity comes a different set of variables and challenges in design, and a different set of potential solutions. "You can tilt, you can have a multi-copter," Stein said. "Or, you can have a lift plus cruise design like we're doing—a system that takes off vertically, but as soon as you take off and want to start moving forward, you'd actually turn off those motors."

An added benefit of this design is that it's easier to maintain and cheaper to run. "We are talking about very simple motors that have almost no moving parts," Stein said. "So straight away, your maintenance costs really go down."

The design also fixes common hovering-related issues. "Hovering consumes a lot of energy and also makes a lot of noise," Stein said, which isn't a major part of Eve's eVTOL design. "You only hover for several seconds before you start transitioning towards cruise flights." It means that compared to a helicopter, Eve's aircraft have an up to 90% reduced noise footprint.

Though one of the early use cases for Eve will be airport to city centre transfers, Stein thinks it is only a starting point, which Stein spoke on at 2023 SXSW Festival in Austin, Texas.

"Say that one day you need to be back earlier because its your kid's birthday," he said, "or you have two different meetings in two different parts of town, or you decide to move away from being close to the office so you can live in a bigger house, or you work from home and go to the office four times a month. These are all great use cases for what we are doing."[4]

These new aircraft could also provide an important tool for city planners and administrators, as it's increasingly no longer the case that everything in a city happens in a single city centre. Instead, cities are becoming either polycentric, with multiple centres of activity, or dispersed across a wide urban area.

One good example of both tendencies is Orlando, Florida. Kyle Shephard, the city's director of intergovernmental relations, appeared on the same SXSW panel as Stein in 2023 to explain how eVTOLs could fit into Orlando's transport architecture.

"We're very spread out, but we've also got these really dense activity centres," said Shephard. "We've got this polycentric urban form—a very dense downtown, America's second largest university, the second largest convention centre in the United States with the Orange County Convention Centre, Universal Studios which is more than doubling in size now, Lake Nona Medical City, and Walt Disney World, the largest single-site employer in the world."

As Stein and Shephard explained to the audience in Austin, Eve has been working with the City of Orlando to map out how eVTOLs might connect the city's different activity centres and with what kind of infrastructure. "You need to bring the ecosystem together, and you've been playing that role of catalyst," Stein said of Shephard. "What we're doing is bringing the partners together, be it city representatives or infrastructure providers."

For Shephard's part, he noted that Eve's ability to be that connector came from practise, building off a similar approach the company developed at an infrastructure summit in Melbourne, Florida. "We had our mock-up there so we could even stimulate the flow of passengers with the people developing the infrastructure," Stein said, "be it the energy providers, people looking at the vertiports, city representatives or technology providers."

Another example is the San Francisco Bay Area. United Airlines, which has a hub at San Francisco International Airport and is an investor in Eve,[5] is working with Eve on an Urban Air Mobility (UAM) network,[6] which can potentially connect economic hubs like Palo Alto, Cupertino, San Jose, and Oakland with San Francisco.

Currently the Bay Area ranks 15th worldwide for traffic congestion, while commuters spend an average of 97 hours in their cars a year.[7] Meanwhile, another study by Melanie Rapino and Alison Fields of the US Census Bureau identified the Bay Area as the region with the highest percentage of '"mega commuting" in the United States (travelling 90 or more minutes and 50 or more miles to work).[8]

But serving sprawled out urban areas is only one of many use cases for Eve. In fact, the company already has orders for more than 3000 eVTOLs, many of them coming from outside North America.

"We announced a partnership with Kenya Airways,"[9] Stein said, "and they have an innovation arm called Fahari Aviation. That's always an opportunity. When you're talking about urban air mobility, it's not only for wealthy countries."

Though Kenya's capital Nairobi is another example of a dispersed city where Eve could be put to use, eVTOLs could also be used to take tourists from regional airports to safari lodges, or to connect rural areas to towns. Fahari Aviation also wants to look at how Eve's aircraft might be used to transport cargo.

With customers in Europe, Asia, Latin America, North America and Africa, Eve's footprint is fully global—and its customers have a variety of different business models. "Some are airlines like United, in the US you also have Republic Airlines and Skywest," Stein said. "You have helicopter operators like Helisul here in Brazil, we have ride sharing services like Blade— different businesses, different models."

Eve's growing customer base led investment bank JP Morgan to conclude that Eve was the "main winner" of the 2023 Paris Air Show, the biggest industry trade event in Europe that year. At the show, Eve inked orders for another 80 aircraft, bringing its order book to 2850 eVTOLs at a value of $8.6 billion.[10]

One announcement signed in Paris was with Widerøe Zero, the sustainability incubator of Norwegian airline Widerøe. Eve and Widerøe Zero originally agreed to develop eVTOL networks in Scandinavia in November 2021.[11] At the Paris Air Show, Widerøe Zero expanded on that partnership, and announced that the network would run with 50 eVTOLs.[12]

WIDERØE EYES EVTOLS TO CONNECT RURAL COMMUNITIES

According to Andreas Aks, Widerøe Zero's CEO, the partnership with Eve was interesting on both sides because Widerøe had a somewhat unusual application for eVTOLs.

"There is no need in Norway to fly across the city," Aks said. "It takes you about 20 minutes by subway through the capital of Norway, Oslo. So there is no big need. We want to explore how eVTOLs can be used in a rural setting."

"We have 40-45 airports spread out on islands around the coast," he continued, "essentially connecting rural communities to cities. And beyond that, there are smaller islands next to them. So people are spread out and living on these islands." As such,

Aks saw in Eve a way to provide "a very valuable service to the rural communities on the islands in Norway."

Widerøe Zero is also looking ahead to a deadline in 2040, when domestic flights in Norway will need to be fossil fuel free, though Aks points to two advantages Norway has when it comes to making that goal a reality.[13] The first, he says, is that Norwegians are already comfortable with the idea of electric powered transport, as 80% of cars sold in the country are electric already.[14]

"This has been pushed by a combination of public measures, political measures and [customer will]," Aks said. "The focus on sustainability has been high for a decade or more. People in general care a lot about the environment and want to do whatever they can."

The second factor, according to Aks, is that 74% of Norwegian flights cover fairly short distances. "We're talking less than 300 kilometres," he said. In other words, the typical distance-related obstacles that hinder first-generation electric, hybrid-electric and hydrogen-electric in other markets are irrelevant in Norway.

Of course, Eve's eVTOLs are only one part of Widerøe's strategy to meet that 2040 deadline. It will also need to replace its fleet of Dash 8 turboprops, specifically any that fly into regional airports around Norway.

Though it makes little economic sense for an aircraft manufacturer like Embraer to make planes specifically for a small market like Norway, which only has a population of five million people, the Energia project has still provided a way for Widerøe to make sure its customers' needs are heard.

That's because Widerøe is part of Embraer's Energia customer advisory board, which advises the Brazilian aircraft manufacturer on the wants and needs of customers in various markets all over the world, making sure the next generation of aircraft can be as much of a global solution for sustainability issues as possible.

HOW EMBRAER WORKS WITH CUSTOMERS TO BUILD BETTER AIRCRAFT

Historically speaking, customer input in the aircraft design and manufacturing process has been critical for Embraer, and the company considers this collaborative approach as part of its DNA.

"We have been doing airline advisory boards for many, many years," said Affonso, Embraer's Senior Vice President of Engineering and Technology Development. "The airline advisory board is a C-Level meeting, so it's a very high-level meeting of several airlines. We try to have the same people participating in all the meetings so we create this group and community spirit."

According to Affonso, the group meets twice a year to discuss many granular design questions which will have big effects in markets around the world. "What is the sweet spot in terms of range?" Affonso asked. "What do you think of the economics? Would you accept slightly higher operating costs to have more range or more comfort?"

In addition to this valuable customer feedback, these advisory boards also serve as invaluable networking sessions where senior airline executives can interact with their peers in an informal setting. "They can hear their colleagues from other airlines give their opinions," said Affonso. "It's not only Embraer that benefits. Each of the members of the group benefits from the experience."

With its Energia aircraft coming into service in the next decade, Embraer is already convening other airlines to help it shape the development of this next generation of zero emissions aircraft. "We invited airlines from North America, South America, Europe, Asia Pacific," Affonso said. "Basically, a global footprint to discuss different things—what would be the ideal size, what would be the application for each aircraft size, [as well as] the availability of green energy and hydrogen."

According to Rodrigo Silva e Souza, Embraer's Vice President

of Marketing, these customer advisory forums have been crucial
—and he has been in more than a dozen of the meetings himself.

"Requirements like seat capacity, range, take off performance,
and maintenance requirements—these are essential in normal
product development," Souza said. "[But for] novel technologies, they are even more important. [On our] advisory boards,
we have over 25 people participating, over 20 airlines giving
their input from different parts of the world with different business models and backgrounds."

All of this input, Souza says, is invaluable to ensure that the
Energia line truly serves the needs of its customers all around
the world.

ENERGIA OFFERS ZERO EMISSIONS REGIONAL FLIGHTS

As mentioned, Eve's overall mission is to serve dispersed urban
environments or smaller communities without airports, all using
a battery electric architecture.

The Energia family of aircraft, however, has a different
mission of serving regional routes and replacing many of the
kerosene-powered turboprops, such as those currently used by
airlines like Widerøe. The architecture Embraer has chosen here
will first be hybrid-electric and later hydrogen-electric.

The shift from kerosene-powered to hybrid-electric turboprops will involve increasing seat capacity from four to 30 and
eventually 50 passengers, while increasing the range from 100-
200 to 500 nautical miles.

These changes will result in a noise reduction of up to 60% as
well as reductions in CO_2 emissions of 30% using regular jet fuel
and 90% using SAF. Embraer expects to accomplish this with its
19 and 30-seater E19-HE and E30-HE early in the next decade.[15]
These will be followed later by the launch of the H19-H2FC and
the H30-H2FC, hydrogen-electric aircraft again in 19 and 30-seat
variants.

These planes will offer even greater sustainability benefits as compared to Embraer's current kerosene-powered turboprops, namely a 70% noise reduction and no CO2 emissions whatsoever.

Looking further ahead, Embraer hopes that the 30-seat aircraft it has planned will serve as a springboard to launch an even bigger plane in 2040: a 50-seat regional aircraft called the E50-H2G which will operate via a dual fuel gas turbine engine, using either hydrogen or SAF as fuel.

MAKING ENERGIA FLIGHTS CHEAPER THAN ELECTRIC CAR RIDES

Through its customer advisory boards, Embraer has learned what airlines want from its new aircraft and has ranked all the different design priorities by order of importance—and perhaps unsurprisingly, cost of operation has emerged as the most important factor. "Of course we need to develop more sustainable solutions," Souza said, "but they also need to make economic sense."

Fortunately, there is extensive research showing that aircraft with next generation technologies will be cheaper to maintain. A 2021 paper by the US Renewable Energy Laboratory estimates that as compared to kerosene-powered engines, hybrid-electric aircraft have maintenance costs that are 20% lower.[16]

For their part, Embraer says their own hybrid-electric aircraft won't only be cheaper for airlines—in fact, Energia flights could also cost less for *passengers*, potentially even less than a comparable trip in an electric car. Comparing a 200-300 nautical mile trip by car and by hydrogen fuel cell aircraft, Embraer estimates that the regional aircraft route will be 2.5x as fast and 25% less expensive, all while emitting 25% less CO2 per passenger than if the same trip was made by an electric car.

An additional benefit that often goes unmentioned, Souza said, is the convenience factor. "The person driving the car might need to sleep over in a hotel and come home the next day," he said. If the same trip were made by plane, that person could be back on the same day.

With all this in mind, Souza says the next-most important customer criteria are product characteristics, particularly range of flight. "It doesn't work if one of these new aircraft is too limited in terms of range. [They] need to have significant range to provide operators with flexibility. And of course they need to operate in different types of weather."

After cost and range, airline customers are concerned about the reputation and expertise of the company developing these new kinds of aircraft. But this is an area where Embraer has a real advantage.

"It's not only about the aircraft, it's about the support," Souza said. "It's good to rely on a credible OEM to make sure that passengers feel comfortable with the new technology."

Affonso echoes Souza's confidence. "Embraer has over five decades of experience in the commuter and regional segments. That gives us real world knowledge of the complete lifecycle of these aircraft, from conceptualisation to development and certification, to product support, phase out and replacement."

With customer feedback in mind, and allowing for the natural cycle of aircraft replacement, natural growth and sustainability mandates like the one in Norway, Embraer has already identified a need for at least 4000 of its new regional aircraft by 2035. However, that demand could be as high as 20,000 aircraft due to the cheaper operating costs and other benefits Embraer has projected for its new aircraft.

To accomplish all this, Arjan Meijer, the President & CEO of Embraer Commercial Aviation, says that getting even more people to fly in a cheaper, cleaner way is absolutely key.

"We like to call our business aviation, but the real product we're supplying is connectivity," Meijer said. "One of the risks in the industry as a whole is that we just keep moving to bigger and bigger aircraft, and we keep dropping off the smaller cities from the maps. We're actually going backwards on connectivity."

According to Meijer, these new changes in sustainable aviation tech will help fix that issue. "This could [lead to] a new future, allowing airlines to fly smaller airports in a fully green manner."

WORKING TOWARDS 100% SAF CERTIFICATION

The Energia concept covers 19, 30, and potentially even 50-seat aircraft. But Embraer also produces larger aircraft, particularly private business jets and its commercial E-Jet family. As with Energia, Embraer is currently working on certifying these aircraft to run entirely on SAF as well.

In pursuit of this goal, Embraer is already at work streamlining operational efficiencies on the E-195 E2, its longest-range and highest-capacity aircraft.

According to Meijer, the technology is already there to make the aircraft burn 25% less fuel. "This can already be grabbed and is being employed as we speak today," he said. After that, the next step is further integration of SAF technologies. "Sustainable Aviation Fuel is probably the lowest hanging fruit. It's a pretty big part of the solution."

In July 2022, Embraer completed a test flight of its E-195 E2 running entirely on SAF, proving that its engines and aircraft were capable of doing so.[17] However, Meijer recognises that there are still issues with SAF when it comes to cost and supply. "We really have a long way to go as an industry."

To stimulate SAF production and meet Brazil's mandate of burning only SAF blends by 2030, Embraer has signed an agreement with Raizen, a subsidiary of Shell Aviation, who has agreed to help.[18]

According to Meijer, SAF is also the answer to decarbonising the business jet sector, which is a particularly important concern for Embraer. In addition to its other aircraft, the company also makes the Phenom 300, the world's best-selling light jet of the past decade.[19]

In executive aviation, fliers pay for flexibility and are not restricted to fixed routes between cities. Though this arrangement works well for customers, it creates all kinds of logistical challenges for airlines and airports when it comes to decarbonising the sector.

While business executives often use private jets to cover long distances, Meijer also doesn't see hybrid-electric or electric propulsion systems as a viable short-term solution. "When you look at the requirements of executive jets, solutions like electric and hybrid-electric are much harder to apply," he said.

Creating the necessary hydrogen infrastructure to serve business jets will be similarly challenging, which is all the more reason, according to Meijer, for executive aviation to focus primarily on SAF for the time being.

"Executive aircraft are just employed completely differently," he said. "For those aircraft to be flying on hydrogen, that's going to be a much more distant future."

LOOKING TO THE FUTURE

While the industry has made a lot of progress, Meijer says that much more is still needed. "In the past 60 years, aviation has reduced emissions by 80% per seat mile," he said. "But our industry needs to achieve the same level of emissions reductions as the past 60 years in the next 30 years, to put the challenge in perspective."

Accomplishing that goal means the aviation industry won't be able to take a fixed approach, and will need to use every technology available. "Focusing our resources and efforts solely on one particular technology, be it hydrogen or SAF or electricity, is not going to work," Meijer said. "This is the big challenge, not just for Embraer but for the whole industry. A holistic approach will be the quickest way to deliver the change required."

As demonstrated by Embraer, that approach involves looking at what the market needs first before matching that need with the right net-zero technology. Similarly, instead of focusing on showy announcements with unrealistic deadlines and targets, the company has prioritised a step-by-step approach using customer input to develop each of its technological solutions over time.

"Embraer is a company that wants to deliver what we promise," Meijer said. "And we want to underpromise on what we finally deliver. We're not in the market of selling sweet stories. When we set targets, we want to achieve them."

"With the demand for energy services growing even larger, we are at a pivotal moment if we are to reduce global warming," Meijer said—and looking at Embraer's net-zero roadmap, it's clear the company is looking at every possible solution. "It's challenging," he said, "not easy. But it's tangible, and we believe it's achievable."

✈ KEY LESSONS FROM EMBRAER

1. **The mission defines the architecture.** Rather than start with the technology, Embraer starts with the business and use cases. It then looks at what technological solution can best meet customer needs.
2. **It's not about aviation, it's about connectivity.** Embraer's solutions bring mobility closer to people. Through Eve and the Energia family of aircraft, Embraer offers a future where more people can fly, more cheaply and greener, than ever before.
3. **Bring the customer with you.** With Embraer's airline advisory boards, customers feed into everything from range to seat capacity. That means that new aircraft are built with the customer in mind.
4. **There is no silver bullet.** Rather than betting on just one technology, we will need every tool in the net-zero tool box for the industry to reach its 2050 target.

5. **Look at how you can open up new markets.** With Eve eVTOL, Embraer is looking at completely new markets, ranging from connecting dispersed cities, to giving people on Norwegian islands a new and faster way to connect to the mainland.

SIX
JETBLUE'S AMBITIOUS PUSH TO DECARBONISE AVIATION

DESPITE BEING ONLY the sixth largest airline in the United States, JetBlue has one of the most ambitious net-zero programmes in the industry.

While almost all airlines follow the ICAO (the UN body that regulates aviation) target of becoming net-zero by 2050, JetBlue intends to hit that milestone 10 years early, by 2040.

Even though JetBlue may have been one of the first to commit to this ambitious target, Sara Bogdan, the airline's head of sustainability, strongly believes it won't be the last.

Bogdan is one of a growing group of industry figures who recognise that the pressure on fossil-fuel emitting industries like aviation will only increase as the effects of climate change are felt more and more. "My personal opinion is that we're all going to have to move [our goals] up and accelerate our work," she said.

In support of her belief, Bogdan cites the 2023 IPCC Report, which warned that climate impacts on people and ecosystems are more widespread than initially thought.[1] Bogdan also believes that events like the record temperatures experienced in the United States throughout the Summer of 2023 will also concentrate more minds on the need to move faster to a non-fossil-fuel-based future.

JetBlue's 2040 net-zero commitment was made in the middle of the COVID-19 pandemic, when travel restrictions turned much of the airline industry upside down. However, despite the challenges that the pandemic placed on the airline, its long term sustainability planning efforts didn't stop, as shown by the airline's commitment to Amazon's Climate Pledge.[2] Spearheaded by the eponymous retail giant, this is an agreement among major companies to reach net-zero carbon by 2040.[3]

JetBlue is so far only one of three airlines to sign the climate pledge, the others being Alaska Airlines and Harbour Air, a small airline that runs seaplanes on the British Columbia coast out of Vancouver—but JetBlue's focus on decarbonisation goes back even earlier than this headline-making decision.

In 2016, JetBlue signed an agreement for the delivery of biofuels at its JFK Airport hub in New York.[4] In the same year, the airline created venture capital fund JetBlue Ventures, which as we will go on to show in the second part of this chapter, invests heavily in sustainable aviation startups.

With a route network stretching into the Caribbean, JetBlue has also been active in promoting coral reef preservation. This has included donating flights to the Nature Conservancy for scientists to conduct research.[5]

Like Bogdan, JetBlue CEO Robin Hayes recognises the need for airlines to take action sooner rather than later, identifying it as both the right thing to do and a business imperative. Hayes' proactive stance on aviation and climate change led to him being recognised as the best CEO for airline sustainability in 2018.[6]

In a 2020 interview on Bloomberg TV, Hayes spoke on the thinking behind these environmental commitments:

More and more customers are becoming aware of the environmental impact that aviation has, and they want the industry to respond. And if we don't, we'll see the impact in demand longer term.[7]

In a Q4 2019 earnings call, Hayes also pointed to the so-called flight shaming movement in Europe, which has been trying to paint air travel as being socially unacceptable due to the carbon emissions that result from flying.[8]

"The issue presents a clear and present danger if we don't get on top of it," Hayes said. "We've seen that in other geographies, and we should not assume that those sentiments won't come to the US."

Though Hayes recognises that there are substantial costs and challenges associated with aviation's quest to carbonise, he thinks airlines should also consider the other side of the question. "What will the cost be if we aren't making these investments?" he asks.

Hayes is also optimistic, believing that growth can be reconciled with sustainability. "We envision a future of aviation that is widely available and affordable, but sustainably operated. This is why we are investing in industry-changing technologies including SAF and new aircraft technologies that have the potential to dramatically reduce lifecycle emissions associated with flying."

And while acknowledging the criticism environmentalists make that SAF is expensive and resource-intensive, Hayes feels that this can be solved, pointing to the year on year increase in renewable energy supplies, which is helping other industries decarbonise. "As the ground industry electrifies there should be more biomaterial feedstocks and renewable refineries that can be diverted to make SAF—rather than renewable diesel, where most is diverted today."

As a result, in January 2020, JetBlue became the first US airline to work with Neste, one of the largest SAF providers in the world, to add SAF on flights out of San Francisco. It also committed to carbon offsetting for all US domestic flights, which make up the bulk of its network.[9]

In July 2021, JetBlue announced a further set of decarbonisation measures. Among these was an agreement with SAF producer World Energy to use 1.5 million gallons of blended SAF at Los Angeles International Airport (LAX) for three years, accounting for around 5% of the airline's fuel demand at LAX.[10]

SCIENCE-BASED TARGETS DRIVE JETBLUE'S DECARBONISATION EFFORTS AND VISION FOR CLEANER SKIES

JetBlue's 2040 commitments are underpinned by something called science-based targets (SBTs). SBTs are used to describe emissions reduction goals that are in line with what the latest climate science says is necessary to limit global warming to 1.5°C above pre-industrial levels.

The company that validates these targets is the Science Based Targets initiative (SBTi).[11] Founded in 2015, SBTi's members are CDP, The United Nations Global Compact (UNGC), the World Resources Institute (WRI), and the World Wide Fund for Nature (WWF).

JetBlue had its 2040 decarbonisation road-map approved by SBTi in December 2022.[12] As part of that roadmap, JetBlue intends to achieve a 50% greenhouse gas reduction per Revenue per Tonne-Kilometre (RTK) by 2035 as measured from 2019 as a base year. Per-seat emissions will therefore be cut in half in just over a decade.[13]

It's an ambitious target, made all the more challenging to achieve considering that various decarbonisation solutions have largely not yet scaled.

"That was a scary part of this commitment," said Bogdan. "We know we're going to do everything we can, but we still don't know exactly how the technology and supply will be available for us to get there."

Bogdan breaks the 2040 commitment down into the following measures:

- SAF will have to do most of the heavy lifting. According to Bogdan, it is "going to be about half of the puzzle," and she recognises that the airline has a long way to go in terms of ramping up its operations to meet that target, with a key challenge being increasing SAF availability. The first goal will be to have SAF comprise 10% of JetBlue's total fuel use by 2030. JetBlue now has agreements in place with Neste, World Energy, and Shell for SAF supply. From 2027 onward, the airline also hopes to see Air Company's e-fuel made out of CO2, hydrogen and renewable energy come on stream, with JetBlue Ventures being an Air Company investor.[14] JetBlue also signed MOUs with Ametis and Fidelis New Energy's Grön Fuels in 2022. Meanwhile in July 2023, JetBlue Ventures announced that it would be participating in United Airlines' Sustainable Flight Fund, where different airlines and travel companies pool resources to help foster the development of SAF.[15] This is an excellent example of companies that are otherwise competitors coming together to tackle the wider industry challenge of climate change.

- Changes are also being made to make the entire fleet more fuel efficient. This includes taking delivery of new aircraft like the Airbus A220 that reduce emissions by 35% per seat as compared to the aircraft they are replacing. For now, however, JetBlue hasn't factored in the introduction of any new next generation aircraft with non fossil-fuel propulsion systems. Bogdan says that this is deliberate, because JetBlue needs aircraft capable of carrying 100+ passengers, which next-gen aircraft can't yet do. "There is a lot of uncertainty in that we don't know if we are going to have large electric or hydrogen aircraft," Bogdan said.

- JetBlue is also making operational improvements, electrifying ground equipment and pushing for air traffic control modernisation so that aircraft fly more fuel efficient routes and spend less time taxiing and waiting to land. JetBlue estimates that current Air Traffic Control inefficiencies account for as much as 12% of fuel burn and resulting emissions. As a result, it is calling for a transition from the United States' ageing radar technology to GPS-based technology, which would allow for greater efficiency, more consistent flight planning, and improved on-time performance for all travellers as an added benefit.

- Finally, though carbon offsetting will continue to play a role in JetBlue's net-zero journey, it is no longer as central to the airline as it was in 2020. At the time, "we wanted to do something big, because we knew customers and our stakeholders cared," Bogdan said. As Bogdan explains, when JetBlue made the original commitment to offset all domestic flights, it was "the best tool [they] had." However, in light of the SAF agreements JetBlue has since signed, the airline has adjusted its strategy. "The world of sustainable aviation is closer than it was," she said. "The time [is] now to take our investments and funds that we [were] putting into offsets and redirect them into SAF." Though Bogdan says that JetBlue will rely on "some degree of offsetting," the company hopes to keep it as "small as possible."

Underpinning all of the above is a focus on the internal culture of the airline, wherein managers are encouraged to make sustainable choices and decisions at all times.

"We're giving leaders across the operation the tools to understand the short and long-term sustainability impacts of their decisions," Bogdan said, considerations to be weighed in addition to business and financial impact. "They can make decisions that are not only best for the organisation but best for the planet."

While JetBlue is looking to increase the available supply of SAF through agreements with companies like World Energy, it is also giving passengers the chance to voluntarily offset their flights with SAF.

In March 2023, the airline launched a platform powered by Norwegian company CHOOOSE, which allows customers to estimate the CO_2 impact of their flights and then select if they want to offset it with SAF purchases.[16]

This partnership with CHOOOSE supplements a programme called Sustainable Travel Partners for the corporate sector.[17] Launch customers have included Salesforce and Deloitte, who purchase SAF certificates for employee flights.

According to Bogdan, these two programmes address the fact that "corporate customers have their own net-zero targets," and being able to environmentally mitigate staff travel helps towards that; these motivations differ somewhat from those of individual travellers.

"Some [travellers] just really care, and they want to be able to add a couple more dollars to help further the SAF market," Bogdan said. As a result of these two programmes, JetBlue now has dedicated funds guaranteed to go only to procuring SAF, according to Bogdan. "That has actually been [a huge help]," she said.

MAKING SUSTAINABILITY VISIBLE TO CUSTOMERS

Of course, customers can't tell the difference about whether their flight is powered by SAF or not, as the experience is much the same either way. "We talk so much about emissions," Bogdan said. "We're an airline, so it's what people think of. But something we also think about is that customers can't see [the use] of SAF, so it's always been hard to communicate."

Because of this, according to Bogdan, the airline is doing a lot to make the cabin more environmentally friendly, as it is an improvement that customers *can* see. These efforts include an onboard waste recycling programme, which was launched over 10 years ago.

While Bogdan says one of her responsibilities as the airline's head of sustainability is to make sure the sorting of in-flight waste happens correctly, she acknowledges that an even better solution would be to generate little to no waste in the first place.

This is where JetBlue's new transatlantic routes to London, Paris, and Amsterdam have served as something of a test-bed. "We had the opportunity to redesign the whole cabin experience," Bogdan said.

For example, Economy passengers on JetBlue's transatlantic flights now receive amenity kits, which as an industry norm are generally only available to passengers in the more expensive cabins. Produced by amenity kit maker Formia, these kits are made from platinum silicone, a more sustainable version of silicone.

As these kits are oven, fridge and microwave safe, once the passenger is back home, they can be used for everything from storing food to carrying around beach toiletries, and are thus reusable.[18] "I actually still use it at home to store vegetables," Bogdan said. "It's an alternative to a plastic bag, essentially."

Similarly, Bogdan says that across JetBlue's entire network, the airline has been removing single use plastics across its catering range.

HOW A JETBLUE-SPIRIT MERGER COULD BOOST SUSTAINABILITY EFFORTS

As of writing, JetBlue is responsible for 5% of US domestic air travel—but if its proposed merger with Spirit Airlines goes through, it will be responsible for even more.

In 2022, JetBlue bid $3.8 billion for Spirit. The result of the merger would be the creation of the fifth largest airline in the US, accounting for 9% of the country's air travel market.

Though the deal is still facing regulatory hurdles, including objections from the US Justice Department at the time of writing, Bogdan sees a successful merger as something that will help aviation sustainability in the United States.[19] "At only five percent of domestic flying, there is only so much impact that we can have," she said. "With Spirit, we [will be] able to expand that."

With the merged airline, Bogdan also believes that her sustainability efforts will get "a bigger seat at the table." In fact, she feels that JetBlue is an example of how airlines can decouple carbon emissions from growth. "Air travel is so important to society," she said, "[but the industry] has a sustainability problem that has to be solved."

By committing to net zero by 2040, Bogdan says JetBlue is providing a positive example. "We envisage a future that allows people to explore the world," she said, "but while having dramatically reduced the impact that goes with it."

According to Bogdan, the key will be continuous improvement rather than perfection. "On day one, the best you can do is acknowledge a challenge," she said. "Next, study and transparently report the current state. From there, set meaningful yet achievable targets. And then the really fun work begins: executing the solutions to improve."

Pushing those solutions forward is something that both JetBlue and JetBlue Ventures are now focused on.

HOW JETBLUE VENTURES DRIVES INNOVATION IN TRAVEL AND BEYOND

In 2016, JetBlue launched JetBlue Ventures, an airline venture capital fund aimed at investing in innovative air-travel related technologies, that today has a particular focus on sustainable aviation solutions.

The initiative garnered significant attention within the industry. In fact when Airbus, the giant aircraft manufacturer, decided to establish its own venture capital arm named Airbus Ventures it drew inspiration from successful existing models, one of which was JetBlue Ventures.

"We took the JetBlue playbook because we thought they were doing it very well," said Paul Eremenko, former Airbus CTO from 2015 to 2018. "They were one of the first, if not the first, to strike the right balance."

The balance Eremenko refers to is the optimal point between operating as a Corporate Venture Fund (CVC) and a pure financial venture capital fund, as each has pros and cons when it comes to supporting startups.

Financial venture capital firms like Andreessen Horowitz, Sequoia Capital, and Accel Partners are common in Silicon Valley and are known for their agility and speed.

"They have no domain expertise," Eremenko said, "but they move really fast. They can make decisions, and they have a lot of flexibility when it comes to investment terms and the cheques they write."

On the other hand, CVCs are typically backed by large corporations who *do* have some kind of domain expertise—as well as a vested interest in the success of startups they invest in.

In addition to being able to spot technologies and products that can benefit their own businesses, the industry expertise and brand recognition of CVCs can also help attract partners, customers and additional investors. The issue, Eremenko points out, is that CVCs suffer from the same problem as any large organisation: they can be slow and overly bureaucratic.

Because CVCs require significant internal sponsorship, decision-making is often delayed, and investments tend to be comparatively small. "That's been the dichotomy," Eremenko said.

JetBlue Ventures, however, seemed like an exception. They behaved like a typical Silicon Valley venture capital firm in terms of decisional autonomy and swift action, but they also had corporate alignment and domain expertise.

That's why when Paul Eremenko set up this new company, Universal Hydrogen, JetBlue Ventures was one of his first ports of call for investment.

Universal Hydrogen is dedicated to developing logistics for hydrogen-powered flights and retrofitting existing turboprop aircraft with hydrogen-electric conversion kits. JetBlue Ventures participated in a $20.5M Series A round in the start-up in April 2021.[20]

"They're a pleasure to work with," Eremenko said. "They bring you the best of both worlds."

TRAVEL TRANSFORMATION THROUGH TECH AND SUSTAINABILITY INVESTMENTS

Since 2016, JetBlue Ventures has become a pioneering airline-backed venture capital fund in Silicon Valley. With a focus on transforming travel through emerging technologies, the fund's initial priorities included areas such as the Internet of Things, machine learning and big data.

Amy Burr, the President of JetBlue Ventures, explained the fund's general mandate with the following question: "How can we change travel through emerging tech?" While the fund occasionally invests in later-stage ventures, Burr said that the focus is on the early stages. "Series A is our sweet spot," she said.

The Series A is a significant round of investment following initial seed funding that is crucial to fueling a company's growth.

By targeting this stage, JetBlue Ventures actively engages with startups that are still in development though not unproven, providing support as they scale and attract customers.

As of July 2023, JetBlue Ventures has made 46 investments across various domains. Examples include direct air capture company Avnos,[21] digital fuel management platform i6,[22] and the weather forecasting company Tomorrow.io.[23]

While JetBlue Ventures originated from JetBlue, projects supported by the fund don't necessarily have to benefit the airline directly, according to Burr. In fact, only about a third of the investments made by Burr and her team directly relate to JetBlue.

The remainder focus on forward-looking and disruptive innovations aimed at industry-wide transformation. Many of these align with sustainability technology, a growing area of interest for the fund (hence the company's investment in e-fuel maker Air Company).[24] "The focus on sustainability tech has really shifted over the past seven years," Burr said. "For us and for everybody."

Climate tech in general has been resilient in attracting funding, even as other sectors have experienced declines. PwC reports that over a quarter of venture capital funding in 2022 was directed towards climate tech.[25] At the same time, JetBlue Ventures' parent company JetBlue has set its own ambitious net-zero target for 2040, exceeding the industry target of 2050 by a decade.[26]

JetBlue CEO Robin Hayes' passion for achieving net-zero carbon goals is a major influence on the fund's investment approach, according to Burr. "He encourages us to make investments that aid the industry, even if they're not directly beneficial to JetBlue," she said.

JetBlue Ventures distinguishes itself not only through its internal significance and growth as a venture capital entity but also by its long-term perspective on sustainability investments.

"We think about what's going to move the needle in five, 10, 15 years for our industry, JetBlue, other airlines and the travel industry," Burr said, "and we invest our money there."

One of those forward-looking investments is in Universal Hydrogen.

UNIVERSAL HYDROGEN: THE NESPRESSO OF ZERO EMISSIONS AIRCRAFT

According to Burr, Universal Hydrogen caught JetBlue Ventures's attention for their smart approach, which includes realising the potential of hydrogen-powered flight while also dealing with the infrastructure issues of getting hydrogen to airports.

"Hydrogen is tricky," Burr said. "To build a hydrogen aircraft takes a long time and a lot of work. There are regulatory approvals and all those things. In addition, you actually have to have hydrogen available at an airport on a regular basis. We don't have hydrogen pipes to airports at this point, so even if you had a hydrogen aircraft that was miraculously ready to fly, you really couldn't fly it."

"We love Universal Hydrogen because they're doing two things that we think are super important," Burr continued. "Number one, they're building a conversion kit—so you have an aircraft and you convert it to a hydrogen propulsion system. But in addition, they're dealing with the logistics. Because their hydrogen is packaged in a pod that is plugged into the propulsion system, it's easy to transport and it's easy to maintain. It's easier to deal with, so they're making progress on two pieces that come together to make hydrogen feasible in aviation."

Paul Eremenko, Universal Hydrogen's Co-Founder and CEO, is an industry veteran, with CTO stints at both Airbus and engine maker United Technologies—but he also has heavyweight Silicon Valley experience, with experience as Director of Engineering, Advanced Technologies and Projects at Google.

Still, rather than keep building his career at legacy aviation firms, he was more interested in co-founding a new company trying to decarbonise aviation with hydrogen. According to Eremenko, the reason for that was simple: he could see that radical solutions were needed to deal with aviation's ever-increasing share of greenhouse gas emissions.

"Aviation puts out as much pollution or CO2 as the country of Germany," Eremenko said. "It's not the biggest, but it's a sizable contribution." And that number is growing. "Aviation traffic volumes double every 15 years," he continued, "so aviation is a victim of its own success."

As such, the spotlight of climate change is shining on the industry more and more, and there's a danger that air travel will be curbed. "I think that would be terrible for the industry," Eremenko said, "but I also think it would be bad for the world. [Aviation has] created a huge amount of economic opportunity. It's the key driver of globalisation, of cultural exchange."

All of this led Eremenko to think about what could be done to enable the industry to reach true zero, where aircraft emit no greenhouse gases at all, instead of net zero, where emissions are offset in other ways.

The only answer he could find was to substitute the fuel. "If you look at the list of fuels," he said, "hydrogen is right at the top. It's the lightest energy carrier outside of nuclear fuels, and aviation is the most weight-sensitive application."

According to Eremenko, hydrogen is also a better solution than SAF. "[Hydrogen] is a true-zero solution, because the fuel is produced using renewable electricity," he said. "This is green hydrogen and water electrolysis, breaking water molecules into hydrogen and oxygen with renewable electricity. And then it's put through a fuel cell on the aircraft, which emits nothing but water."

A tangible sign of that progress came on March 2, 2023. That day, a Dash-8 turboprop dubbed Lightning McClean took off from Moses Lake, Washington and flew for 15 minutes, reaching an altitude of 3,500 feet.[27] It set a new record for the biggest hydrogen-powered aircraft ever flown.

During the flight, an electric motor powered by a hydrogen fuel cell ran beneath Lightning McClean's right wing. For safety reasons, the left wing had a standard turboprop engine that offered additional power. The test pilots were able to throttle back the conventional engine and cruise primarily on the one hydrogen-powered engine during the second circuit over the airport.

Universal Hydrogen's aim with the test flight of Lightning McClean was to demonstrate the safety and reliability of hydrogen-powered aircraft and to prepare for its commercial introduction in regional airliners by 2025.

Much like US/UK company ZeroAvia,[28] Universal Hydrogen is retrofitting regional aircraft by developing a modular hydrogen fuel system that can be added onto their existing airframes.

The system consists of two main components: Hydrogen capsules that can be transported to aircraft (using trucks or rail) and a fuel cell powertrain, the actual propulsion system that converts hydrogen into electricity. Though Lighting McClean was a de Havilland Canada Dash 8-300 aircraft, the first aircraft the company is looking to retrofit is the ATR-72-600 regional turboprop.

As of mid-2023, the company had an order book of almost 250 conversions from 16 different customers.[29] These include an order of 75 aircraft conversions from Connect Airlines, a new carrier serving Canada and the Northeast USA that aims to be carbon neutral.[30]

In February 2023, Air New Zealand brought Universal Hydrogen on board as one of the partners in its Mission Next Gen Aircraft programme, wherein the New Zealand airline is assessing how non-fossil-fuel-powered aircraft can be used in its route network.

But even though these conversion orders and the successful

test flight put Universal Hydrogen in the news, the company is still most focused on hydrogen logistics. In fact, Eremenko said the name Universal Hydrogen was chosen to mark the business as more of a utility company that gets hydrogen to airports and aircraft. Still, he recognises that there is no point supplying the company's modular hydrogen capsules if there are no aircraft equipped to fly them.

"I like to analogise our business model to the Nespresso coffee model," Eremenko said. "We're not a hydrogen producer. We buy the hydrogen in the same way Nespresso doesn't grow their coffee, they buy the coffee. They use the existing freight network to deliver that convenient form factor to the end user. We do exactly the same thing."

Of course, in the beginning, Nespresso had pods but had no coffee machines in which you could use them. "They had to build the first coffee maker," he said. "Otherwise, [the pods would be] completely useless. And so, for our first product, we are in effect building the coffee maker, which is the retrofit conversion kit for the ATR-72."

Today, you can choose from dozens of different Nespresso-compatible coffee machines, and that's the same endpoint Eremenko wants to reach with hydrogen and aviation.

"We don't want to be an engine company, we don't want to be a retrofit company, and we don't want to be an aeroplane company," he said. "We are a hydrogen fuel services provider using this modular form factor to make every airport hydrogen-ready."

In the future, Eremenko sees Universal Hydrogen becoming the hydrogen fuel supplier for a completely new generation of narrowbody aircraft—and the work the company is doing now will allow it to springboard its technology from regional planes to larger ones.

"More than half of aviation CO_2 emissions today come from the A320 and 737 family of aircraft," Eremenko said.

Both Airbus and Boeing will need to replace these venerable

aeroplanes with a new design, starting development in the late-2020s and entering passenger service in the mid-2030s. Making their successors hydrogen aeroplanes is a golden opportunity—perhaps the only opportunity—for aviation to get anywhere near meeting Paris Agreement emissions targets without having to curb aviation traffic volumes.

When these completely new aircraft are ready to be flown, Universal Hydrogen will be there with the network in place, supplying them with the fuel that they need.

EP SYSTEMS: LEADING THE CHARGE IN SUSTAINABLE AIR TRAVEL WITH CUTTING-EDGE BATTERIES

Alongside hydrogen, battery electric power is the other main way to power aircraft without using fossil fuels. Battery electric power is a clean and quiet way to fly, but it has a number of limitations.

Most importantly, batteries still suffer from low energy density. To power even a small aircraft requires a heavy battery, which limits the planes to short flights. One way to overcome this is for battery technology to advance. To that end, JetBlue Ventures is investing in Utah-based Electric Power (EP) Systems, one of the most promising battery makers, as a way to help kickstart that development.

"The electrification of aviation will grow in importance as a method for reducing the carbon footprint of the industry as a whole," Amy Burr said. "Electric Power Systems will play a key role in the development of electric aircraft. They have energy storage systems, fast charging stations, and ways to support electric propulsion systems." And according to EP Systems President and CEO Nate Millecam, the company has a great working relationship with JetBlue Ventures.

"There are a lot of synergies between our two organisations," Millecam said. "JetBlue Ventures is one of the pioneers in aerospace venture funds. They really pioneered it and showed people how to do it well, and so we feel honoured to be a part of their portfolio."

The partnership also feeds into JetBlue Ventures's goal of transforming the entire aviation experience through new sustainable technologies, which is an ongoing discussion in the industry.

"Unless you have a battery system that not only meets the very high safety requirements as well as the technical requirements in terms of weight, power density, cycle life and economics, you really don't have a sustainable solution," Millecam said.

Before becoming CEO of EP Power Systems, Millecam worked for a number of aerospace companies including Honeywell, where he helped develop lithium-ion batteries for the flight control electronics of the Boeing 787 Dreamliner, an experience which showed him the potential of advanced battery technology in aviation. Later, he joined a power semiconductor company that acquired a battery company working on electric motors.

Recognizing the value of the technology, Millecam cofounded EP Systems in 2016 with a focus on developing and certifying lithium-ion batteries for aviation. Since then, Millecam says that they have "developed and certified more lithium-ion batteries than anybody in the world."

Currently, EP Systems is working with a number of companies looking to decarbonise air travel through electric propulsion systems. One example is REGENT, which is developing a new kind of sea glider that glides above the water like a hovercraft but has wings in the style of an aircraft.[31]

REGENT's 12-passenger sea glider Viceroy is expected to enter service by mid-decade—and thanks to EP Systems batteries, it is designed to carry 12 passengers for 180 miles on a single charge. "What they're doing at REGENT is very innovative," said Millecam. "They're doing a distributed electric propulsion system, but they're doing it in sea gliders, which are certified under the Coast Guard versus the FAA. This gives them a faster path to market."

Another customer is Ampaire, which is retrofitting existing regional aircraft with hybrid-electric propulsion systems, beginning with a Cessna Grand Caravan. In 2022, Ampaire broke the record for the longest hybrid-electric flight, when a demonstrator aircraft flew for 1135 miles non-stop from California to Kansas.[32]

"[Ampaire is] really focusing on hybridisation," said Millecam. "It's a very complex hybrid architecture, but it has incredible gains in weight, is very reliable and has a lot of redundancy and safety. It's a really brilliant architecture, but they're doing it on a Caravan. The Caravan is a legacy platform and it's certified."

The company's ability to work on two very different types of aircraft, such as Ampaire's and Regent's, is one of its unique selling propositions.

"A lot of the reason why skilled engineers come to EP Systems is we always tell them, 'If you go to one company, you work on one propulsion system and you'll follow that through your whole career, and you'll certify it,'" Millecam said. "But if you come to EP Systems, you get to work on everybody's.'"

One of the biggest growth areas for EP Systems is to develop batteries for the growing eVTOL sector.

EP Systems is currently collaborating with eVTOL partners like South Korea's Plana, Japan's SkyDrive, and Supernal, which is part of automaker Hyundai. Millecam knows the battery technology exists to allow these aircraft to fly; the challenge is in producing them.

"We've been doing development to prove that the technology is viable for the last eight years," he said, "and the good news is it's viable. [But] the scale at which we have to produce these [batteries] is an order of magnitude higher than anything we've ever seen in aviation."

As Millecam explains, producing an aircraft battery is not like producing a car battery. The former must be able to take passengers thousands of feet in the air without issue—and planes can't simply "pull over" if something goes wrong, which means the bar for quality is exceptionally high.

"Aviation is not going to alleviate its requirements for safety or certification down to automotive levels or other consumer levels for batteries," Millecam said. "So, we have to rise to those standards while rising with the production rates. There's a lot of testing. There's a lot of inspection. There's a lot of data collection that has to happen."

JETBLUE VENTURES' EARLY INVESTMENT IN JOBY AVIATION PAYS OFF AS ELECTRIC AIR TAXIS TAKE FLIGHT

Just as eVTOLs are a big growth area for EP Systems, JetBlue has made its own big play in the space by coming on board as an investor in Joby Aviation.

California-based Joby is developing a piloted, four-passenger aircraft capable of travelling up to 150 miles on a single charge at a top speed of 200 mph. The aircraft will be electrically-powered and operate with zero emissions. As of 2023, the company had raised over $1 billion in funding and has over 1,000 employees.[33]

"Part of how we think about Joby and eVTOLs in general is that it changes how travel happens," said Burr, particularly of the first and last mile of the journey. "It's part of the travel experience, [so] our customers will take Joby aircraft to an airport, which will help them have a more seamless journey and cut down on their carbon footprint."

Of course, there are other synergies between JetBlue Ventures and Joby. Bonny Simi, Joby's Head of Operations and People, is a former airline pilot who went on to become JetBlue Ventures's first President from 2016-2020.

The firm's investment in Joby happened under her watch,

positioning JetBlue Ventures as an early investor in eVTOLS as part of a funding round in early 2018.[34]

"We believed that electric propulsion would fundamentally change aviation, just like jet propulsion did back in the 60s," Simi said. "There hasn't been a whole lot of innovation in the aviation space, but we saw that changing, so we wanted to invest."

According to Simi, the electric aviation space had far fewer companies at that time than there are today. "Now, of course, there are hundreds but back then, it was about 50. And we ruled them out for a number of reasons. We wanted to make sure [the aircraft were] piloted, that [the companies] had the right management teams and the right technology."

All of these criteria led them to Joby, which ticked all the boxes. "Back then, the company was only 50 people," Simi said. Above all though, Simi explains it was Joby's leadership team that convinced JetBlue Ventures to invest. "It was because of [CEO] JoeBen Bevirt and his vision."

Following the investment, Simi joined Joby's board to have a front row seat as the company grew, which led to her joining full-time. "The company was growing so much and getting ready to go public," she said. "At the same time, of course, there was of course COVID, which was a challenging time for airlines and Joby needed a lot of help because they were going to be going public, so it was a very natural transition."

Though Joby was actually founded in 2009, Simi says that the pace of the company's development has been anything but slow. "It is a monumental task to design and certify an aircraft, so we are working on many parallel streams. It's been a fast and furious and exciting journey."

Due to enter commercial service by 2025, Joby's aircraft have now completed over 1000 test flights.[35] However, Joby's big airline partner isn't JetBlue, but rival US airline Delta, who have come on board as an investor and are working with Joby to integrate their electric air taxi flights into Delta's operations.[36]

The fact that JetBlue Ventures is still so closely involved with Joby is a prime example of how it works autonomously from its parent company, always considering how its investments can improve and disrupt travel more generally—though, of course, their interests can overlap.

"I would love for Joby and JetBlue to have an agreement together," Burr said. "That would be amazing. But JetBlue has other things on their mind right now, and that's fine. We never tell startups that they shouldn't work with other airlines. If they work with other airlines and they're successful, that's success for everybody."

For their part, Joby is excited about Delta. "We're very passionate about this partnership," Simi said. "It's solving one of the most painful pieces of the journey: getting to and from the airport. Imagine being at home and opening an app on your phone and instantly booking a ride to the airport."

As Simi explains, this arrangement would mean calling a car to pick the passenger up and take them to a nearby vertiport. After that, they would fly up and over the traffic to the airport, leaving only a short walk to their seat on the plane. It's one of several deep integrations that Delta and Joby are collaborating on.

"Both Delta and Joby envision an experience where customers can choose to book their seat in the Joby service at the same time they're booking their Delta ticket," Simi said. "Our whole focus is very, very customer-centric. How can we make this seamless and enjoyable end-to-end?"

Joby's vision, however, is bigger than bringing people to and from airports. Instead, it hopes to disrupt urban transportation in general by making it more affordable.

Speaking at the 2023 SXSW Interactive Festival in Austin,[37] Joby CEO JoeBen Bevirt even discussed developing air taxis and vertiports to serve people living in urban areas.

Part of the thinking is that a larger Joby-Delta network will not only result in better connectivity but also economies of scale:

"The more [air taxis] we have," Bevirt said, "the more convenient [urban transport] becomes, and the more savings we can provide."

Eventually, the cost of travelling in an eVTOL should, according to Joby, even be comparable to taking a trip in an Uber or Lyft, and their partnership with Delta is helping to make that possible.

The end result, according to Bevirt, should be transformative for commuters in major urban centres. "We are so locked into our existence of driving along the roads," he said. "When you rise above that, you see the beauty of the world, and it's really profound. It gives every day a new perspective. That's one of the pieces I am beginning to understand—what a significant impact that will have on the quality of people's daily lives."

FROM STARTUPS TO SCALE-UPS: JETBLUE VENTURES'S EVOLUTION IN DRIVING DECARBONISATION

It goes without saying, the investments mentioned above are not typical quick-return Silicon Valley plays. Instead, all of these companies are taking different paths to decarbonising aviation, a goal which will take years of design, production and certification. This shows that JetBlue Ventures is in this for the long-haul and is investing in companies that have the potential for making a real difference.

As a result, while most CVC funds last only four to five years, JetBlue Ventures is already "well past that," according to Burr. Instead, the company's eye is on the 2030s. "In 10 years, we will probably be substantially bigger," she said. "We've made 46 investments to date, so we'll probably have a lot more assets under management and a lot of really great companies."

As the fund evolves, Burr also says the investment strategy will evolve along with it. "We'll probably be thinking more about later stage companies, as a company like ours grows a little older," she said.

Though Burr thinks there will likely be greater divergence between the strategic investments JetBlue makes to advance its own interests versus those made to benefit the entire industry, she is confident they will continue to find the right balance—and helping entrepreneurs make guilt-free and fossil-fuel-free flights a reality will always be a goal.

✈ KEY LESSONS FROM JETBLUE

1. **Be an early mover.** JetBlue set ambitious sustainability goals like net zero by 2040 years ahead of the industry norm of 2050, which established them as a leader in the space.

2. **Always engage your customers.** JetBlue gave customers visibility into sustainability via cabin initiatives and opportunities to directly fund emissions reductions, efforts which educate and empower customers.

3. **Partner widely.** JetBlue collaborated across the value chain with SAF producers, industry groups, and corporations to drive change through collective action. They aim to lead by example, but they plan to bring others along. JetBlue Ventures taking part in United Airlines' SAF is also a key example of how different players in the industry can pool their resources towards helping to solve a common challenge.

4. **Get buy-in from the top.** Sara Bogdan's sustainability efforts have been powerful, but part of what has helped is the support of CEO Robin Hayes. Hayes has been open about the business need for the airline and the industry at large to decarbonise, realising the urgency of the problem and thus underlining the company's sustainability efforts throughout the entire corporate culture.

5. **Find the balance between corporate alignment and agility.** JetBlue Ventures has been successful by striking a balance between operating as a Corporate Venture Fund (CVC) and a financial venture capital fund. This means that they have been able to maintain their domain expertise and corporate alignment, while also behaving like a Silicon Valley venture capital firm with autonomy and swift decision-making.

6. **Leverage domain expertise.** CVCs backed by large corporations can leverage their industry expertise and brand recognition to attract partners, customers and additional investors. As such, JetBlue Ventures benefited from JetBlue's domain expertise and connections in the travel industry, giving it a competitive edge.

7. **Take a long-term perspective on industry transformation.** JetBlue Ventures demonstrates a long-term perspective on industry transformation by investing in emerging technologies and sustainability-focused ventures. The fund actively engages with startups during their early development, providing support as they scale and attract customers. This approach allows JetBlue Ventures to position itself as a pioneer in airline-backed venture capital while contributing to the transformation of the travel industry more broadly.

8. **Address infrastructure challenges as well as technological innovation.** JetBlue Ventures' investment in Universal Hydrogen highlights the importance of addressing not only technological innovation but the supporting infrastructure required for its implementation. Universal Hydrogen is developing hydrogen-powered flight as well as tackling infrastructure changes associated with

hydrogen availability at airports. By developing both a conversion kit for retrofitting existing aircraft and a modular hydrogen fuel system, Universal Hydrogen has a comprehensive plan to make hydrogen-powered aviation feasible.

SEVEN

ETIHAD'S FOCUS ON NET-ZERO EMISSIONS TODAY

THE EMIRATI SCIENTIST BREAKING BARRIERS IN AVIATION SUSTAINABILITY

"WHEN YOU LOOK at the UAE 51 years ago, we came from humble beginnings, we lived in tents, we were nomadic bedouins. And look at us now!" As Mariam Musallam Al-Qubaisi, the head of sustainability for the country's national airline, Etihad Airways, points out, the changes that have taken place in the United Arab Emirates (UAE) over the past half-century since the country gained independence have been remarkable.

Al-Qubaisi herself personifies the changing face of the UAE-an environmental engineer and scientist with multiple academic qualifications, Al-Qubaisi holds an MPhil in Engineering for Sustainable Development from the University of Cambridge.

After graduating, she taught environmental science at Zayed University, focusing on crucial issues like water policies in a country where freshwater resources are scarce. But she felt she needed to do more than just talk about sustainability in theory. "I wanted to practise what I preached," she said.

So, Al-Qubaisi started applying to UAE companies for

sustainability roles, and luckily, Etihad offered her a position. It was a significant milestone as she became the first Emirati national to hold the head of sustainability role in the airline, a position previously held by expatriates.

At Etihad, Al-Qubaisi works with expatriates on a daily basis and acknowledges their valuable contribution to the development of the country. "We owe a lot to expats. They trained us and taught us. We shouldn't underestimate their importance in the UAE's development," she emphasises.

However, Al-Qubaisi says that being an Emirati woman as the face of sustainability for Etihad has distinct advantages. Al-Qubaisi believes it helps her navigate Middle Eastern culture and achieve results. It also allows her to tie the work she does at Etihad with her role as an expert on the country's task force on cleaner fuels.

Since 2019, Al-Qubaisi has spearheaded numerous sustainability initiatives for the airline, as well as serving on industry-wide working groups with organisations such as IATA, the trade association of the world's airlines, and the ICAO, the UN body overseeing aviation.

Al-Qubaisi's tenure as head of sustainability for the UAE's national airline comes as the country finds itself in the climate change spotlight. That's because the UAE is the 2023 host of the Conference of the Parties of the United Nations Framework Convention on Climate Change (COP28), an annual gathering of world leaders, industry, and NGOs to agree on measures to combat global warming.

Since it is one of the world's biggest producers of fossil fuels, having the UAE host the event has been controversial, which Al-Qubaisi recognises.

"Some people are sceptical about the intentions of the United Arab Emirates," she said in an interview with Times Aerospace,[1] "[but] our government is taking [climate change] extremely seriously."

Among other efforts, the UAE has committed to tripling their rate of renewable energy production until 2030,[2] and establishing a research and development centre to scope out how the UAE can be a major exporter of low-emissions hydrogen. Etihad Airways, as the national airline, plays a critical role in the country's journey towards a greener future.

THE GREENLINER INITIATIVE AS A SUSTAINABILITY TEST-BED

Etihad Airways took an interest in sustainability as early as 2011, when it started researching how Sustainable Aviation Fuel (SAF) could be used for its extensive long-haul routes.

That work came to fruition in 2019 when the company flew a Boeing 787-Dreamliner from Abu Dhabi to Amsterdam, partially fuelled by SAF. The milestone also marked the birth of the "Greenliner" programme at Etihad, a nickname for the variously outfitted Boeing 787-Dreamliner the company uses for special eco-friendly flight tests.[3]

The Greenliner initiative coincided with Al-Qubaisi's arrival at Etihad. She remembers that when it came to sustainability, "there was an expectation that we needed to make sustainability less of an accessory and more of a necessity."

As a result, the Greenliner initiative has been core to the airline making sustainability more of a priority. Collaborating with industry giants Boeing and GE, the Greenliner initiative has involved testing technologies such as SAF and eco-friendly in-flight products across its entire fleet of Boeing 787s, spearheaded by the specially themed Greenliner-liveried aircraft. The Greenliner initiative has encompassed various notable achievements:

- During the delivery flight of the aircraft from Charleston to Abu Dhabi in January 2020, a 30% blend of biofuels was utilised. Additionally, the flight served as a testing ground for multiple emissions-reduction measures, leveraging tools like the Jeppesen FliteDeck Advisor app to optimise the flight path in real-time.[4]

Furthermore, the Etihad crew implemented modified descent procedures on their approach to Abu Dhabi, resulting in further fuel savings.

- To mark Abu Dhabi Sustainability Week in 2020, Etihad completed a special eco-flight to Brussels, including a blend of SAF. This was followed up by another eco-flight to Brisbane in Australia.

- In October 2021, the Greenliner achieved a 72% reduction in CO_2 emissions on a flight from Abu Dhabi to London's Heathrow Airport. It did this through a combination of buying the equivalent of 38% SAF for the fuel used in the flight and by using a range of other measures, such as delivering baggage via electric tractors.[5]

WORLD ENERGY'S BOOK AND CLAIM SYSTEM ENABLES ETIHAD'S NET-ZERO FLIGHT

Following that successful Greenliner flight to London in 2021, the airline wanted to see if it could up the sustainability stakes even further.

Jörg Oppermann, Etihad's Vice President of Midfield Operations, explained the company's thinking at the time. At first, Etihad wondered if the October 2022 COP27 climate summit in Sharm El Sheikh, Egypt might present an opportunity.

"[Our first thought was,] 'Okay, let's do a net-zero flight,'" Oppermann said. "'Let's fly delegates from the United States to Sharm El Sheikh and have the maximum amount of SAF on the aircraft.'"

Though the plan sounded promising, Oppermann said that the company soon realised doing this would not be straightforward. To do so, Etihad would need to get approvals from the relevant authorities; it would also fly a flight crew to Egypt on a separate flight. "And that was not sustainable," Oppermann said.

As a result, Etihad proceeded with a net-zero flight but opted for a more feasible strategy: integrating it into one of the airline's regular scheduled departures from Washington, DC to Abu Dhabi.

With a more straightforward USA to UAE flight, Oppermann said that Etihad was onto the next question. "Where do I get sustainable aviation fuel in the United States?' We reached out to one fuel supplier after the other, [and] we realised that SAF is actually only really commercially available in California," he said. This is due to the generous incentives that exist in California, meaning that in 2021, the state had 80% of the world's SAF supply (which we discuss in the Introduction).

The question for Etihad was: could the SAF be transported from California to Washington Dulles International Airport? According to Oppermann, the trucking costs alone would have resulted in an additional 20 tonnes of CO_2 emissions and $50,000 in logistics costs.[6]

Just as Etihad was looking for answers to these questions, Al-Qubaisi received a call from Adam Klauber, a sustainability expert at alternative fuel company World Energy.

According to Al-Qubaisi, Klauber asked if Etihad would want to operate a net-zero flight using 100% SAF, through Book and Claim. This is an industry mechanism where you buy the equivalent amount of sustainable aviation fuel for your flight, but it goes into the general industry supply system.

Al-Qubaisi says that this was "music to my ears." However, as she'd just given birth the week before and was still on maternity leave, she put Klauber in touch with Oppermann. As a result, Etihad worked with World Energy on the initiative.

Established in 1998, World Energy started producing SAF in 2018 and has since made it its primary focus.

As part of its efforts, World Energy acquired a century-old oil refinery in Paramount, in Southern Los Angeles County, and invested $2.5 billion to convert it into a SAF production facility. The company also purchased a 47-mile pipeline network, which it is upgrading to enable direct pumping of SAF to Los Angeles International Airport (LAX), located approximately 20 km from the plant.

The aim of this $2.5 billion investment is to make the benefits of SAF available for airline customers around the world, even though the supply is in California. One of those customers was Etihad, who displaced the equivalent amount of fossil fuel from its 2022 Washington, DC-Abu Dhabi flight, through the purchase of SAF.

World Energy's Adam Klauber foresees Book and Claim being around for years to come: "People in the industry say, 'Book and claim is kind of a cool and novel thing, but we won't need it very long,'" he said. "Actually, we *will* need it."[7]

Klauber cited two reasons for its continued importance: the limited availability of SAF outside regions like California and the limitations of current aircraft certifications. At the time of writing, commercial aircraft flown by Etihad, such as the Boeing 787-Dreamliner or Airbus A350, are only certified to carry a 50% blend of SAF, meaning the remaining 50% still comes from kerosene derived from fossil fuels.

A Book and Claim system allows airlines to purchase enough SAF to displace all the fossil fuel emissions it uses in these flights, making them net-zero.

For his part, Oppermann agrees with Klauber's assessment. "[Book and claim] is the way forward for the foreseeable future and by the foreseeable future, I mean around 10 years."

SCALING UP SALICORNIA: UAE ACADEMIC RESEARCHES GAME-CHANGING JET FUEL

The 10-year time frame Oppermann describes is a long time, it is also just enough for some of the UAE's ambitious national plan to come to fruition as it applies to SAF production.

"[The UAE has] a very aspirational road map that assumes that by 2030 we will have a supply of seven hundred million tonnes of sustainable aviation fuel," Al-Qubaisi said, noting that it will include many different pathways and feedstocks.

Among these methods is one that involves the cultivation of a simple desert shrub, one that UAE-based academic Dr. Alejandro Rios Galvan believes holds the potential for SAF at scale.

As the director of the Sustainable Bioenergy Research Consortium and Professor of Practise at the UAE's Masdar Institute of Science and Technology, Dr. Galvan is leading the Seawater Energy and Agriculture System (SEAS) project, which in 2019 produced a small quantity of SAF that Etihad was able to use on a demonstration flight[8] from Abu Dhabi to Amsterdam in 2019.[9]

SEAS utilises the Salicornia plant, which grows in salt marshes and beaches, as a feedstock for producing SAF. Unlike traditional SAF production methods, SEAS's method doesn't use arable land or freshwater resources, making it ideal for the water-scarce UAE.

"We take seawater, bring it in, and use that water for a fish farm," Dr. Galvan said. "As the fish are growing, they generate waste, and that waste goes into the water. So, this water must be changed frequently."

In commercial fish farms, that waste water often goes back into the sea—though Dr. Galvan notes that doing this leads to "effluent from the fish or shrimp farms coming back into the farm, and therefore killing the animals because of the accumulation of waste." For a normal commercial operation, "these losses represent millions of dollars in lost revenue."

"Rather than dumping the waste back into the ocean, we do something with it," Dr. Galvan said. "We use it as a liquid fertiliser to regrow these plants. They can grow with seawater on desert sand, and the nutrients are not coming from the soil. They are coming from the fish waste."

As the plants grow, Dr. Galvan's team harvests them and extracts vegetable oil, which is then turned into paraffinic kerosene, an alternative jet fuel—but what makes SEAS even more remarkable is its potential for carbon neutrality.

According to Dr. Galvan, as the plants develop and absorb carbon dioxide, the sea water used to grow them passes through mangrove forests, helping them to grow as well. Mangroves can flourish in saline environments, and as the mangrove plant is effective in absorbing CO_2, this leads to an extra environmental benefit.

As a result, if assessed over a full lifecycle, the carbon emitted during cultivation and fuel burning becomes offset by the carbon absorbed during plant growth. "If you use the system in an integrated way," Dr. Galvan said, "you basically have a carbon neutral fuel."

Crucially, unlike other feedstocks used for SAF, Dr. Galvan believes that the Salicornia solution is one that can actually scale, which he explained at length while speaking at the MRO Middle East Conference.[10]

"There are 25.5 million square kilometres of desert and arid fields around the world with access to brackish or salt water," he said, adding that even 0.01% of that area could result in the 449 million litres of annual SAF production—the amount needed to fuel 65% of aviation by SAF by 2050, according to the International Air Transport Association (IATA).

"Clearly, this won't happen overnight," Dr. Galvan said. "It's a huge challenge. But it's one we need to address in a place like the UAE, where we do not have plentiful fresh water or arable land."

UAE'S SUNSHINE POWERS AVIATION DECARBONISATION

While the UAE may face challenges in terms of water and arable land, it does possess one valuable resource in abundance: sunshine.

As solar energy, sunshine has a key role to play in aviation's net-zero journey. Solar energy can be used to produce green hydrogen, achieved where an electrolyser splits water (H_2O) into oxygen (O_2) and hydrogen (H_2).[11]

That green hydrogen can then be used to make so-called e-fuels, which is SAF produced by mixing green hydrogen with captured CO_2. That green hydrogen can also be used directly as a fuel source in aircraft.

The UAE has set ambitious goals to become a major green hydrogen producer. By 2031, they aim to produce 1.4 million tonnes of hydrogen, with a further target of 15 million tonnes by 2050. This will involve establishing hydrogen production facilities known as "oases," with two planned by 2031 and three more by 2050.[12]

The UAE has dual objectives with this strategy: capturing 25% of the global green hydrogen market and leveraging the produced hydrogen to decarbonise various industries, including aviation.[13]

Etihad—in collaboration with Siemens Energy, Japan's Marubeni Corporation, and UAE clean energy firm Masdar—has been exploring the potential of producing e-fuels from green hydrogen since 2021. As such, the UAE's big production plans could result in the airline having a cheap and abundant supply right at its doorstep.

Since green hydrogen is a key component of e-fuels, Etihad also has a partnership in place with Twelve, a California-based startup making this new kind of fuel. The partnership aims to result in a demonstration flight using Twelve's fuel onboard an Etihad aircraft.

According to Twelve, their synthetic fuel could reduce CO_2 lifecycle emissions by up to 90% for Etihad.[14]

Al-Qubaisi said that the initiatives being pioneered by the SEAS programme, and the agreement with Twelve are of both medium as well as long term importance to Etihad.

The airline's route network is largely long-haul, and it will be decades before alternative technologies like hydrogen or electric propulsion systems power anything other than short regional flights. In her view, alternative fuels "will be the norm for at least another 20 years", and as a result, this is where the airline is putting most of its sustainability efforts.

HIDDEN CLIMATE CHALLENGES AND PIONEERING EFFORTS TO MINIMISE CONTRAIL REDUCTIONS

The SAF developed by Twelve or Dr. Galvan's Salicornia project can address an aircraft's CO_2 emissions, but there is another aspect of the aviation industry that receives less attention: the non-CO_2 emissions produced by air travel, consisting of gases and particles such as nitrous oxides (NOx), sulphur dioxide (SO_2), water vapour (H_2O), and particulate matter (soot).[15]

When released at high altitudes, these emissions can have a significant impact on the atmosphere. For instance, NOx and SO_2 can react with water vapour to form sulphate and nitrate aerosols, which can either reflect or absorb sunlight, affecting the climate. Water vapour acts as a greenhouse gas, trapping heat in the atmosphere, while soot particles can absorb sunlight and contribute to warming as well.

Contrails, the white lines visible in the sky created by commercial aircraft, make up the biggest single contribution of non-CO_2 effects to aviation's climate impact. The latest scientific research suggests that contrails account for up to 2.4 billion tonnes of carbon dioxide equivalent (CO_2e) each year,[16] more than double the climate impact of direct engine emissions. Mitigating the impact of contrails could substantially reduce the aviation industry's climate change impact.

Etihad is one of the few several airlines actively looking into this matter, partnering with UK company SATAVIA, which helps airlines develop contrail-avoiding flight plans for its aircraft.

Dr. Adam Durant, SATAVIA's Founder and CEO explained the issue as follows, "everyone has seen these streaks across the sky [produced by aircraft]. These contra clouds are called condensation trails, and they are basically clouds full of ice crystals."

As Dr. Durant explains, at the altitude where aircraft fly, the temperature may be minus 50 or 60 degrees Celsius. As a result, water vapour in the atmosphere forms small ice crystals, which interact with incoming sunlight. "They also interact with heat that's trying to escape to space," he said.

These tiny particles can stay in the atmosphere for tens of hours, effectively forming artificial clouds. These persistent contrails result in a warming effect, holding captured heat from the sun without reflecting sunlight back into space. The impact of this is potentially very large. One study even estimated that contrails account for 57% of the aviation sector's total climate impact.[17]

Fortunately, there's also good news: a small number of flights are responsible for the most persistent contrails. If the aviation industry can identify which flights those are, they could make a very big dent in their climate change impact.

"It's only 5% of all flights that create these long-lived warming contrails," Dr. Durant said. "We want to find places to put aircraft where they're not going to create those clouds. Once you reroute the aircraft, then of course the clouds don't form and you don't have that warming effect."

An industry conference first alerted Al-Qubaisi to the work that SATAVIA, and its founder Dr. Adam Durant, was doing. She was intrigued enough to want to look into the issue in more detail.

Al-Qubaisi could see that the existing literature on the topic was quite scientific and relatively niche. However, she was also encouraged by the fact that most of the papers on the topic were written by academics from top-ranked universities. As a result, "I had a quick call with Adam," she said. "I loved the idea and pushed it to our operations team (to implement)."

Starting with the special October 2021 London Heathrow-

Washington to Abu Dhabi net-zero flight, Etihad has been using SATAVIA's DECISIONX: NETZERO advanced atmospheric modelling software.

This proprietary software allows SATAVIA to generate optimised flight plans that circumvent conditions conducive to contrail formation, reducing their occurrence by up to 60%. Even so, the nature of contrail formation is highly variable, and depends on daily weather conditions influenced by geographical location and seasonal variations.

Dr. Durant estimates that the analysis takes 15 minutes per flight, and typically involves, "small adjustments, a few thousand feet up or down, just to avoid these moist layers." A briefing is then given to the pilot, who follows the flight plan just as they would on any other flight.

Speaking at the COP27 climate summit in Sharm El Sheikh, Dr. Durant explained, that the Etihad-SATAVIA partnership involves analysing the climate impact of all flights on a given day, and developing "a short-list of flights that are going to have long-lived, persistent warming contrails."[18]

After this, SATAVIA requests the flight plans of those small numbers of flights and makes the necessary changes to the routes to mitigate the risk of forming long-lasting contrails.

The success of that initial work has led to Etihad signing a multi-year commercial agreement with SATAVIA. The new multi-year commercial deal will see STAVIA's proprietary contrail prevention technology fully integrated into Etihad Airways' fleet operations.

Etihad pilots will have access to SATAVIA's real-time contrail prevention advisories during take-off planning and while in flight. When the system indicates potential contrail zones ahead, pilots can make informed decisions to reroute around them without compromising safety or efficiency. Over time, the continual use of SATAVIA's targeted guidance will measurably reduce Etihad's overall contrail production.

The partnership also provides Etihad early access to a new

platform being developed by SATAVIA, one which will enable airlines to earn future carbon credits based on contrail prevention and other associated climate benefits. On August 7, 2023, the carbon accreditation programme Gold Standard announced approval of SATAVIA's contrail methodology concept, paving the way for issuance of credits generated via contrail management. When fully deployed, this platform will offer an alternative to traditional carbon offsetting schemes centred around planting trees.

"Our collaboration with SATAVIA illustrates the possibility of credible sustainability advances in day-to-day commercial operations," Al-Qubaisi said. "In 2022 alone, SATAVIA's technology has enabled us to eliminate thousands of tonnes of carbon dioxide equivalent climate impact."

CONSCIOUS CHOICES PROGRAMME EMPOWERS SUSTAINABLE SOLUTIONS FOR BUSINESSES

Though all these investments and partnerships will take time to come to fruition, they will also result in Etihad passengers benefitting from flights with far lower carbon emissions than is currently the case.

However, like other major airlines, Etihad has an important customer segment that needs to show that they are travelling more sustainably right now and not in the future: the corporate travel and business market.

Those businesses and corporations have sustainability goals that they typically report on annually, and they are required to demonstrate tangible progress. That includes a reduction in so-called scope three emissions, the indirect emissions a business generates via its supply chain (or through activity such as business travel).

To address the needs of the business and corporate markets, Etihad has introduced an innovative new program called Corporate Conscious Choices to empower companies and organisations to make more sustainable and eco-friendly travel decisions right now.

"This program demonstrates our strong commitment to decarbonising aviation and reducing our climate impact over the long-term," explained Martin Drew, Etihad's Senior Vice President Global Sales & Cargo until September 2023 who oversaw the initiative.

Corporate Conscious Choices provides a wide range of options for businesses and organisations of all sizes to actively participate in carbon-reducing practises that diminish the environmental consequences of their employee travel and transportation requirements.

First, there is an optional green surcharge added to fares (around 1% of the total cost). This environmental fee goes directly into funding carbon offsetting projects that fully compensate for the greenhouse gas emissions associated with corporate travel flights.

Second, SMEs can enrol into Corporate Conscious Choices and after every flight, businesses will earn Etihad Guest Miles which can be invested in offset programmes or sustainable fuel programmes. The miles they earn will be enough to offset half of the emissions for their business.

"We reward SMEs by giving them Etihad Guest Miles to mitigate and offset their employee travel," Drew said. Those miles are channelled to certified carbon offset projects run by Carbon-Click, Etihad's New Zealand-based sustainability partner.

Third, Etihad's cargo customers as well as other large corporate customers can bulk purchase SAF, which displaces traditional fossil-based jet fuel and directly decreases flight emissions. Meanwhile, individual passengers can utilise their own Etihad Guest Miles to offset personal flights or buy eco-friendly products from Etihad's Reward shop.

Etihad has invested substantially in other environmentally-focused programmes, but corporate clients are demanding sustainable options immediately to meet urgent carbon-reduction goals and react to stakeholder pressures. Conscious Choices meets that need, and can provide a platform for further initiatives aimed at business customers in the future.

FROM SKY TO SHORELINE: ETIHAD'S MILLION MANGROVE MISSION FOR A GREENER FUTURE

A key feature of the Conscious Choices programme has been giving customers easy options to reduce their carbon footprint when flying with Etihad.

This was also the thinking behind a programme that Etihad launched in 2022, wherein booking a seat with extra legroom would result in Etihad planting a mangrove tree on behalf of the passenger in its Etihad Mangrove Forest.[19]

Mangrove trees are extremely effective carbon absorbers, as they sequester four times more carbon than rainforests. Etihad says that a single mangrove tree will absorb up to 250 kg of CO_2 in its lifetime—the same amount produced by an eight-hour flight.

Another benefit is that mangroves help reduce coastal erosion and fortify shorelines. According to the UK's Nature Conservancy, mangroves reduce the height and energy of wind and swell waves that pass through, reducing their ability to erode sediments and damage sea walls and other structures.[20]

For his part, Oppermann stresses that this isn't a conventional carbon offsetting scheme. Instead, it is a Corporate Social Responsibility (CSR) activity, as mangroves are a "signature feature of Abu Dhabi."

"It is a way to bring sustainability to life," Oppermann said, adding that mangroves are a reminder of how important fishing and access to the sea have been throughout the history of the UAE. "You need something people can relate to, which they can grasp and understand."

In addition to granting the passenger more room on a flight, booking one of Etihad's Economy Space seats also results in a mangrove sapling being planted on the passenger's behalf. After one year, passengers receive a special e-certificate with their tree's GPS location, which they can visit when in Abu Dhabi.

Guests travelling in other Etihad cabins can also have mangroves planted in their name using their frequent flyer guest miles. The airline pursued hyper-transparency through this initiative, because not only can those who contribute see exactly where their tree was planted, but also meet the person who takes care of these trees, virtually.

Ultimately, the airline aims to plant over a million mangroves through this initiative, eventually planning to plant mangroves in other areas of the world as well.

THE PATH TO ENVIRONMENTAL AIRLINE OF THE YEAR

Like Corporate Conscious Choices, Etihad's sustainability programme includes various initiatives that seek to offer short-term decarbonisation solutions. Still, it is also laying the groundwork for the future through ambitious green hydrogen and SAF production targets.

Similarly, by focusing on aviation's non-CO2 emissions through its work with SATAVIA, Etihad is breaking new ground in an area that has thus far been absent from many other airlines' sustainability efforts. All of the above has culminated in Etihad being named Environmental Airline of the Year in both 2022 and 2023 in the Airline Ratings Awards.[21]

Geoffrey Thomas, the Editor-in-Chief of AirlineRatings.com, praised Etihad for "its leadership in the push for sustainable flight with its Greenliner Boeing-787 programme." Similarly, Thomas remarked on the airline's "all consuming" approach. "Etihad Airways staff and management are committed to reducing the airline's CO2 footprint and it shows," he said.

As a sign of this, Al-Qubaisi points to the fact that the Operations Division now has responsibility for implementing Etihad's sustainability initiatives. "I don't think you will find that in any airline, and I think this shows how much we are committed to decarbonisation and innovation."

✈ KEY LESSONS FROM ETIHAD AIRWAYS

1. **Avoid creating a sustainability "silo."** As Mariam Musallam Al-Qubaisi stresses, her role isn't just window dressing. She has the actual freedom to introduce and get buy-in for sustainability ideas, and the decision-making process in doing so is fast.

2. **Be willing to test things out.** When Al-Qubaisi put the idea of using SATAVIA's contrail reduction technology to the operations team, they trusted her expertise on the science and expressed a willingness to begin trials. This has since resulted in a multi-year partnership, where something as simple as altering the flight path of a small number of flights can result in a large environmental benefit.

3. **Lay the long-term foundations for decarbonisation now.** The UAE has almost no SAF currently available, but that will change in the next decade as projects such as the Salicornia plant scheme come to fruition. These plans are being made now so that decarbonisation can accelerate in the 2030s.

4. **Keep customers involved and make it easy for them to make sustainable choices.** Through initiatives such as the mangrove tree forest or the Conscious Corporate Choices initiative, Etihad has taken pains to bring sustainability efforts out of the abstract realm and put them directly in front of customers. Doing so is good for team and customer morale alike, and can help spur bigger efforts forward.

EIGHT
SKYTEAM'S SUSTAINABLE FLIGHT CHALLENGE: BRIDGING HISTORY AND INNOVATION IN AIR TRAVEL

THOUGH TODAY you can fly non-stop between London and Perth in 17 hours, air travel between Europe and Australia used to be a much more arduous endeavour characterised by frequent refuelling stops and lengthy travel times.

In fact, even making that journey in under a month was once celebrated as an astonishing achievement. For example, Australian siblings Ross and Keith Smith received considerable acclaim in 1919, securing a reward of £10,000 (equivalent to £660,000 or US $831,000 today) for taking 28 days to fly between Great Britain to Australia.[1]

As a result, the aviation landscape of the 1920s and 1930s bore witness to multiple attempts at shortening the incredibly time-intensive Europe-Australia route. Out of these attempts, the 1934 MacRobertson Air Race is perhaps the best known example. A visionary confectionery tycoon, Sir MacPherson Robertson, pledged £15,000—equivalent to £879,000 or US $1.1 million today[2]—to a competition that challenged competitors to fly between the UK and Australia in record time.[3]

Although a British team emerged as victors, clocking a remarkable (for the time) 71-hour journey in a de Havilland DH.88 Comet, much of the the limelight was on a Dutch team from airline KLM, which secured second place with its Douglas DC-2 dubbed Uiver, meaning "stork" in Dutch.

KLM transformed Uiver's voyage into a routine commercial flight, accommodating three passengers alongside 25,000 pieces of mail. The team made 22 stops en route, ultimately concluding the expedition in 90 hours.

Yet Uiver almost didn't make it, as the aircraft encountered an electrical storm 300 km short of Melbourne, its final destination.

Fortunately, the residents of Albury, New South Wales, lined their cars up at the local racecourse, illuminating a makeshift runway with their car lights, allowing Uiver to land safely. The aircraft resumed its journey the next day and successfully landed in Melbourne.[4]

The exploits of KLM's Uiver crew and aircraft became legendary in the Netherlands, with thousands of spectators greeting the team at Amsterdam's Schiphol Airport when they returned.

Those achievements were still being remembered 88 years later, when they formed the inspiration for a very similar kind of race.

While in 1934, aviation's paramount challenge was to conquer vast distances, in the early 2020s, the industry found itself confronting an entirely different issue: how to maintain the advantages of mobility for future generations while lowering the impact that air travel has on a warming planet.

That conundrum was the genesis of a completely new competition, the Sustainable Flight Challenge.

FROM AVIATION HISTORY TO ENVIRONMENTAL INNOVATION

Founded in 2022 and run by the SkyTeam Airline Alliance, the Sustainable Flight Challenge had a compelling mandate for airlines: could they push their sustainability boundaries by reducing the environmental impact of one specific flight as much as possible?

The idea was that the challenge flights would showcase what the airlines could do, serving as a springboard for even more progress in future years. Of course, it's thanks to the pioneering aviators who flew the Uiver to Australia all those years ago that the initiative came about.

In 2021, an internal working group within KLM called Bold Moves was looking at the issue of sustainability. Maarten Koopmans, one of the Bold Moves members and managing director of KLM's regional subsidiary KLM Cityhopper, remembers it well. "We said to our board in the midst of the COVID crisis, 'Guys, let's come out of this differently than we went in, in the aspect of sustainability.'"

Koopmans says that Bold Moves started with 15 people but soon grew to over 100 participants, all with a wish to preserve the benefits of aviation for future generations, while lessening its environmental impact. Out of the 10 eponymous "bold moves" the team developed, one was the idea of an airline challenge to run the most sustainable flight possible.

One member of the original Bold Moves team was Robin Spierings, a product manager within KLM's Digital Transformation team, who explains the thinking: "[In 1934], people wanted to prove that long distance commercial aviation was possible, but we didn't have the jets that we have today. So we had to break the line of thinking that it was impossible."

Spierings says that this led the Bold Moves team to ask another question. "If back then we proved that long distance commercial aviation was possible, why couldn't we use that same pioneering spirit to see if sustainable aviation is possible? We used the same concept, but in a different time setting and in a different era where there are different problems and issues."

Of course, it wasn't going to be much of a challenge or race if KLM was the only participant. "We couldn't organise a competition, pat ourselves on the back and say, 'Well done, KLM,'"

Spierings says. Instead, other airlines and participants needed to be involved, and there needed to be third party judges.

Since KLM was a member of the SkyTeam Airline Alliance, that seemed like a good place to start—and the Bold Moves team wondered if SkyTeam couldn't take on and own the challenge.

Headquartered in Amsterdam and established in 2000, SkyTeam currently has 20 member airlines that collectively serve 1,050 destinations across 166 nations. SkyTeam members foster cooperation in areas such as network expansion, passenger lounge access, frequent flyer programs, commercial synergies and seamless passenger journeys.

As well as KLM, SkyTeam member airlines span the globe, consisting of Aerolíneas Argentinas, Aeromexico, Air Europa, Air France, China Airlines, China Eastern, Czech Airlines, Delta Air Lines, Garuda Indonesia, ITA Airways, Kenya Airways, Korean Air, Middle East Airlines, Saudia, TAROM, Vietnam Airlines, Virgin Atlantic and XiamenAir.[5] Aeroflot's membership is currently suspended.

KLM's approach to SkyTeam to take on the Sustainable Flight Challenge came at a fortuitous time, as the alliance had been focusing increasingly on sustainability.

According to SkyTeam's Vice President of Marketing and Commercial Mauro Oretti, the increasing resonance of so-called "flight shaming" among European consumers in particular, meant that "it became clear that [sustainability] was something we needed to look at and explore."

However, with the COVID-19 pandemic grounding much of global air travel, SkyTeam had not made as much progress in the sustainability arena as it would have liked. "When the opportunity of the Sustainable Flight Challenge came," Oretti says, "there couldn't have been a better enabler for change."

Oretti says that the downturn in air travel during the pandemic had resulted in "skies with clear air and no noise." If, like SkyTeam, you were based near a major airport like Amsterdam's Schiphol Airport, you could "[feel] the difference."

As a result, Oretti says there was a shift that occurred after the pandemic. "People [were looking] at sustainability with different eyes," he says. "[We knew] sustainability would have to become a much more important ingredient of our work."

SkyTeam then broached the concept with a select group of airline bosses from within the alliance to gauge initial reactions. "All the CEOs were excited," Oretti says, which made getting wider buy-in easier. "An important group of CEOs [was] already engaged from the start."

Once that crucial buy-in had taken place at a senior level, all the pieces started falling into place. "When you are onto something meaningful from a global perspective for the betterment of the world, sometimes magic happens," Oretti says. "It was an alignment of stars on various fronts."

In fact, it took only a month and a half for the idea to circulate within SkyTeam and get approved—and only nine months from approval for the first Sustainable Flight Challenge to take place in May 2022. Given the logistics of coordinating the challenge among airlines worldwide, this was an impressive feat.

Oretti says that the key to getting that first SkyTeam Sustainable Flight Challenge off the ground was Robin Spierings. As one of the original KLM Bold Moves team members, Spierings was seconded to SkyTeam to project manage the initiative.

TAKING FLIGHT FOR A GREENER FUTURE: THE EVOLUTION OF THE CHALLENGE

Once seconded to SkyTeam, Spierings started working with her new SkyTeam colleagues on implementing the first Sustainable Flight Challenge. In doing so, SkyTeam focused on a number of different areas. As SkyTeam knew, the challenge couldn't simply be a race with awards. Instead, it had to provide actual value, with all the insights and knowledge being shared.

"The precondition was that every innovation that would be on these flights would be shared, open source," says Spierings, with the result that every airline would, in a sense, "win" something from the challenge. "Either they get the recognition because they are a front runner, and they are acknowledged because they are best in class, or they learn something because they all get this knowledge and information."

Spierings says that a number of airlines felt the same—they didn't want this to be yet another PR exercise. "I remember that [Delta Air Lines CEO] Ed Bastian said, 'I don't want it to be a media gimmick. I really want us to do this for the right reasons, where we learn from each other."

At the same time, SkyTeam recognised that framing the challenge as a competition would help spur adoption among member airlines. "In all honesty, CEOs are competitive people," Spierings says, "so the fact that there was a small competition going on was appealing as well. It was playful, and it had a different type of energy than the regular type of projects that they were engaged in."

The parameters were then set for the inaugural Sustainable Flight Challenge in May 2022. Participating airlines had to take part between May 1-14 and could enter their flight into one or more of 14 different flight categories.[6]

Those categories included among others best customer engagement, greatest CO_2 reduction across medium and long haul flights, best waste management, and best in-flight sustainable innovation.

Meanwhile, SkyTeam also unveiled a high-profile panel of judges, which included Professor Jan Peter Balkenende, Prime Minister of the Netherlands from 2002 to 2010; Thiongo Ndungu, director at Climate Lead Africa; Zara Rutherford, the youngest woman to fly solo around the world, and many more.

Even so, SkyTeam's initial expectations were modest. "We thought maybe if we aimed for five big carriers or five airlines, that would already be a good start," Spierings says.

After all, as Delta's Chief Sustainability Officer Amelia DeLuca points out: "Operating an airline is incredibly complex.

Every airport kitchen is different. Every country has different regulations. How you source products and the inventory management of it can change, and then you add on top of supply chain constraints."

"In the past, I might have said no to this idea because we don't have X, Y, Z available to scale it," DeLuca says. Ultimately though, the feeling within Delta and among most other SkyTeam member airlines was that they wanted to take part. "It allowed you to take on this really complex problem, and it allowed you for one day and one flight out in the air to just test the art of the possible," DeLuca says.

As a result, 16 out of SkyTeam's 19 airlines ended up taking part in that very first Sustainable Flight Challenge, far more than SkyTeam had originally anticipated. According to DeLuca, "it was just cool to see the entire company and all those airlines really rise to the occasion."

That success then paved the way for an impressive 22 participants to take part in the 2023 contest.[7] This is actually more than SkyTeam's total membership of 19 airlines, as the alliance extended invitations to a wider circle of "friends and family," encompassing subsidiaries and strategic partners.

Those friends and family additions included Endeavor Air, an affiliate of Delta Air Lines, and JamboJet, a subsidiary of Kenya Airways, Shanghai Airlines (part of the China Eastern group) and Aeromexico Connect.

HOW SKYTEAM'S AIRLINES PUSHED THE SUSTAINABILITY ENVELOPE

SkyTeam's airlines showcased a wide array of innovative environmental initiatives, across both the 2022 and 2023 challenges. We've included the full list of 2022 and 2023 winners at the end of this chapter, but here are some of the different sustainability areas that were covered:

Sustainable Aviation Fuel (SAF)

In Chapter One of the book, we detail why SAF made from non-fossil fuel feedstocks is such a central component of the industry's net-zero plans, given that it is a so-called "drop-in fuel" that works with the planes flying today.

As a result, it's noteworthy that half of the participating SkyTeam airlines conducted flights utilising a blend of SAF, among them Air France, KLM, China Airlines, Kenya Airways, and ITA Airways.

In Delta's case, the airline operated a flight from Atlanta to Salt Lake City as part of the first 2022 challenge. The aircraft that was used, a 737-900ER, was powered by a fuel blend that included 400 gallons of SAF. This was a historic milestone, establishing a record for the largest amount of SAF ever utilised on a flight departing from Atlanta.

Reflecting on this achievement, DeLuca highlighted the significance of this flight. "I know we get used to hearing about SAF," she says, "but we have to remember it's still only concentrated in a couple of airports. And so the flight out of Atlanta was quite a feat."

In 2023, Kenya Airways made history by operating a Boeing 787 Dreamliner flight from Nairobi to Amsterdam, timed to coincide with Africa Day on May 25th. This marked the airline's inaugural use of SAF on a long-haul flight, underscoring their commitment to sustainability.[8]

Similarly, Taiwan's China Airlines achieved a significant milestone by conducting its first SAF-fueled flight on a journey from Taipei to Singapore.[9] The aircraft refuelled with 10% SAF for the return leg, as Singapore stands as one of the few locations in the Asia-Pacific region where SAF is readily available.

Bringing Passengers and Staff into the Sustainability Journey

Drawing inspiration from frequent flyers and dedicated staff, SAUDIA, the national airline of Saudi Arabia, placed passenger and employee engagement at the heart of its 2022 and 2023 sustainability challenge entries.

In May 2022, SAUDIA introduced an in-flight sustainability lab on a flight from Jeddah to Madrid.[10] After the meal service, over 200 passengers were encouraged to submit ideas on how flights could become more environmentally friendly. This initiative was complemented by a staff sustainability lab at the airline's Jeddah Headquarters, resulting in over 150 unique sustainability ideas being submitted to SAUDIA.

Building on this momentum in 2023, SAUDIA launched a "Greener Flying" portal, inviting customers and staff from around the world to submit concise sustainability ideas.[11]

The portal allowed visitors to vote on various proposals and showcased ideas already implemented. In a spirit of collaboration, SAUDIA extended the opportunity for other SkyTeam airlines to adopt and adapt this Green Flying Portal for their own use. Both of these initiatives were done in partnership with SimpliFlying.

In 2022, Aeromexico engaged passengers in its sustainability efforts during a Mexico City to Vancouver flight, supported by satellite company Viasat's sponsored in-flight WiFi.[12] Passengers were presented with Aeromexico's sustainable practices, including the use of reusable cups and blankets crafted from recycled plastic bottles.

On-Board Sustainability

While passengers almost certainly won't discern the type of fuel powering their flights, they do notice the amenities provided onboard. This led to a concerted focus on enhancing onboard sustainability during the 2022 and 2023 Sustainable Flight Challenges.

Delta Air Lines introduced new amenity kits for customers on Sustainable Flight Challenge flights, designed to reduce waste by eliminating five single-use plastic items per kit. These kits were developed in collaboration with Someone Somewhere, a Certified B Corporation blending Mexican traditional craftsmanship with innovative products, creating job opportunities for over 250 individuals in vulnerable regions of Mexico.[13]

In 2023, Delta also tested a reusable cup system and new paper cups, aiming to reduce all on-board single-use plastics by 2025.[14]

Vietnam Airlines gifted passengers on a May 2023 flight from Hanoi to Frankfurt souvenir tote bags crafted from recycled life vests.[15] This creative initiative, part of Vietnam Airlines' Sustainable Flight Challenge entry, involved social enterprise Limloop recycling out-of-service life vests into passenger amenity items.

KLM even equipped its cabin crew with new uniforms made from organic cotton and recycled polyester as part of the 2023 Sustainable Flight Challenge. Crew members were also provided with suitcases constructed from recycled plastic bottles, contributing to both sustainability and weight reduction, ultimately reducing fuel consumption.

More Fuel-Efficient Aircraft

As explained in Chapter One, modern aircraft like the Airbus A350 exhibit significantly greater fuel efficiency compared to older counterparts such as the A340. Consequently, airlines have pursued fleet renewal programs, with these newer aircraft taking centre stage in most SkyTeam members' challenge flights.

For instance, in 2022, Air France unveiled its Air France ACT program, aimed at achieving a 30% reduction in CO2 emissions per passenger-kilometre by 2030 as compared to 2019, or a 12% reduction in total emissions.

To demonstrate this objective, the airline operated two flights from Paris Charles de Gaulles hub, one to Montreal using an Airbus A350 and another to Lisbon with an Airbus A220.[16]

These state-of-the-art aircraft consume 20-25% less fuel than their predecessors while significantly reducing noise pollution.

Air France envisions that by 2030, these aircraft will constitute a substantial 70% of its fleet, up from 7% today.

Sustainably-Sourced Food

Global emissions from "food miles" amount to an estimated three billion tonnes of CO2 annually, making it a substantial contributor to global warming.[17]

Consequently, several airlines participating in the Sustainable Flight Challenge prioritised offering sustainably and locally sourced meals to passengers.

China Airlines, for instance, introduced a new "Clean & Green Plant-Based Cuisine" low-carbon menu for passengers on the Taipei-Singapore flight in 2023.[18]

Jointly developed with the Michelin Green Star-winning Yang Ming Spring restaurant, this menu showcased locally sourced, seasonal ingredients, garnering significant interest from passengers, with over half opting for the low-carbon menu.

Kenya Airways also served customers a farm-to-fork in-flight menu, sourcing products directly from local Kenyan farmers and supplemented by fresh herbs from catering partner NAS.[19]

Low Waste Flights

The aviation industry generates approximately six million tonnes of waste each year from passenger flights, with 20% of that waste attributed to discarded passenger meals, according to the International Air Transport Association (IATA).[20] Addressing this issue, Vietnam Airlines collaborated with NGO VietHarvest to redistribute excess food from its kitchens to those in need.[21]

KLM Cityhopper's approach to reduce food waste on its Amsterdam-Trondheim flight was to provide snacks and drinks to passengers at the gate rather than on board.

This strategy resulted in an 80% reduction in food and drink carried on the flight. KLM Cityhopper Managing Director

Maarten Koopmans emphasised the significance of gate catering and recycling, leading to zero waste and the responsible use of materials.

Operational Improvements

In Europe, airlines have been pushing for the implementation of a European Union initiative called the Single European Sky, which looks to harmonise and modernise air traffic control procedures. "If we could get the single European Sky, we'd already be 15% more efficient with less fuel use," Koopmans says.

As a result, KLM Cityhopper's flights to Porto in 2022 and Trondheim in 2023 were designed to highlight the benefits of such initiatives, taking the most direct routes and reducing speed to minimise fuel consumption. According to Koopmans, this was "the quickest slow flight we have ever made to Porto and Trondheim."

Air France meanwhile trialled what it calls eco-piloting techniques, such as taxiing on a single engine while on the ground instead of having both engines running. This comes as OAG figures show that up to 17% of the total fuel burned in a flight comes while an aircraft taxis in or out.[22]

Looking back on the 2022 challenge, SkyTeam CEO Patrick Roux celebrated the achievement of a 50% reduction[23] in CO_2 emissions on several flights. "Overall, the average was a reduction of 15 percent," Roux says.

At the same time, the challenge showed that there are meaningful sustainability improvements that can be realised right now.

As Air France Director of Sustainable Development Vincent Etchebehere said, "When you are talking about SAF, when you are talking about fleet renewal, you are not talking about science fiction. You are talking about concrete, tangible, reachable CO_2

emissions reductions. For me, that was the number one outcome of the challenge."

For Spierings, some of the simpler, less flashy initiatives were the ones that stood out, given that lots of small steps can make a big difference.

"Each and every one in itself might not stand out or seem so special, but it's the combination of all these small things together that can actually lead to, for example, 15% energy efficiency and operational improvements," Spierings says. "With this challenge, we prove that we can do more if we put our minds to it."

THE CHALLENGE IS A MEANS TO AN END

Mauro Oretti concurs that while the individual innovations showcased by participants in the 2022 and 2023 Sustainable Flight Challenges are commendable, it's the cumulative effect of these diverse efforts that truly matters.

To Oretti, the Sustainable Flight Challenge, often viewed as a competition, serves as a conduit for the aviation industry to spotlight and disseminate valuable sustainability concepts. He summarises it as "a means to an end," where the ultimate objective is changing aviation to make it more sustainable.

This is why designing the challenge to be as inclusive as possible, was so important, according to Roux. Recognising that airlines are at varying stages of their sustainability journey and face unique challenges, the competition was intentionally structured to accommodate this diversity.

While in the 1934 MacRobertson Air Race which inspired the Sustainable Flight Challenge, there was only an overall winner (the British team in the de Havilland) and a handicap winner (the Dutch Uiver team), the Sustainable Flight Challenge had 14 categories in 2022 and 24 in 2023.

"We have a jury that can look at 24 different categories of initiatives," Roux says, "so I think there are opportunities for each of our members, whatever their size, to really implement some breakthrough ideas. You look at SAUDIA, you look at Kenya Airways, and they are active and innovative in the challenge. This is not only a challenge for the Europeans or the Americans."

As Roux points out, "We all live on the same planet. And whatever the regulations are [in different countries], we all have to do something."

Spierings said that another factor in "levelling the playing field" was to look at how far different airlines had come. "We wanted to incentivize airlines to stretch themselves. For airlines that already do [sustainability] really well, it might be harder to gain extra improvements than an airline that is lacking a little bit more behind. and has more room to grow. So, we incentivized both overall performance and the biggest improvement compared to baseline. "

Along with making the Sustainable Flight Challenge inclusive, SkyTeam recognised that for the initiative to be truly valuable, the insights and learnings from the challenge flights had to be shared. As Delta CEO Ed Bastian said when the idea was first being discussed among SkyTeam's CEOs, it had to be more than a PR exercise.

This comes as the aviation industry is sometimes criticised for making big announcements about sustainability that aren't always followed through. "It's easy to have a kind of whimsical exercise where you test and experiment things that in the end don't get adopted," Oretti says.

This led to the creation of distinct awards in the 2023 Sustainable Flight Challenge that, according to Oretti, "rewarded the airline that adopted the most solutions from other airlines and the airline whose solution was adopted by the most carriers."

On the back of the Sustainable Flight Challenge, SkyTeam has even created a digital innovation platform, where best practice initiatives can be shared across the alliance.

"All the airlines that participated in the Sustainable Flight Challenge are connected to the platform," Oretti says. "It contains, I believe, 15 or 16 streams ranging from SAF to eco-piloting, from waste management to in-flight improvements."

But not only does this platform include the various innovations rolled out as part of the Sustainable Flight Challenge, Oretti says it has a wider remit in sharing best practices: "For example, pilots who are interested in flight path optimization, those pilots can talk with other pilots."

For those interested in the non-CO2 impact of aviation, such as contrails, the platform is also useful. "You can see who in each airline is looking after contrails, and they can collaborate in this community," Oretti says.

This ethos of collaboration has been enthusiastically embraced by the airlines themselves. "What I love about sustainability as an airline person is that it's the most collaborative thing that I've ever seen this industry do outside of the pandemic," DeLuca says.

"I saw the industry come together during the pandemic to protect the industry, to protect jobs and to protect its customers. Now the same thing is happening in sustainability, and SkyTeam is really facilitating that through this challenge."

Oretti agrees and thinks that SkyTeam's platform can be a model for other efforts. "It can really inspire and can be used by other airlines or even other industries," he says.

TAKING THE CHALLENGE BEYOND SKYTEAM

Extending the initiative beyond SkyTeam is very much the vision. The idea is not to have an initiative where SkyTeam pioneers various sustainability initiatives but keeps them in the group. "We don't want to organise a competition between SkyTeam and the rest of the world," Roux says.

Instead, Roux wants to use the Sustainable Flight Challenge as a springboard that "would enable the industry to accelerate its transition [to a net-zero future]."

Similarly, even if it won't single-handedly bring aviation to net-zero, Spierings sees the Sustainable Flight Challenge growing and evolving. "Do I think this will be around in five years? I absolutely hope so, and I am convinced that this will be of added value to airlines, so that it remains," she says.

Spierings adds that she hopes to "grow it to an independent industry initiative, where other alliances or independent airlines can join," and sees potential for other parts of aviation to get involved.

"A similar type of challenge [could be] set up for airports, or for catering companies, or for maintenance, repair and operations divisions, or cargo," she says. "There's all these different players in the value chain that should have, in my opinion, the same incentive and the same structure to lift the entire industry to a new level."

In all, her work on the Sustainable Flight Challenge has made Spierings optimistic that aviation can solve the major sustainability challenge ahead. "What gives me hope is the willingness of people to come together to collaborate," she says. "It feels as if there is a powerful groundswell of more and more people who want to leave a better planet behind."

Here, Spierings quoted KLM's founder Albert Plesman: "'The ocean of the air unites all people.' I think that really holds true here. It's a feeling of, 'Let's fix this together.'"

For her work in sustainability, Spierings has been selected as one of the 2023 Women of the Future, 50 Rising Stars in ESG. She sees sustainability being treated by the industry in the same way that safety is. Aviation today is the safest form of transport, and that's thanks to it being seen as a collective industry issue, rather than a competitive one.

"We can still compete," Spierings says, "and whoever implements the best, fastest or first will be the one who stands out. But ultimately everyone benefits. I really feel that if we put all these initiatives to practise on a large scale, and prove that [they are] possible on a small scale, we can actually accomplish our climate goals."

✈ KEY LESSONS FROM SKYTEAM

1. **The past can sometimes provide inspiration.** The KLM Bold Moves team drew a parallel between the challenges faced in the past in the 1934 MacRobertson Air Race, and the modern day challenge of making air travel more sustainable. Aviation history provided inspiration to address contemporary challenges.

2. **Collaboration and alliances are important.** As one of the world's major airline alliances, SkyTeam was able to marshall different airlines to take part in the Sustainable Flight Challenge. This demonstrates the importance of different industry groups to drive sustainability initiatives.

3. **Emphasise inclusivity and diverse participation.** The Sustainable Flight Challenge has aimed to include a wide range of airlines, irrespective of their size or geographical location. Airlines were able to participate and contribute, no matter where they were in their sustainability journey.

4. **Share best practices.** The Sustainable Flight Challenge encouraged airlines to share their sustainability initiatives and innovations openly. This sharing of best practices not only fosters learning but also accelerates the adoption of sustainable solutions across the industry. As a result, the fourth key learning is the value of sharing knowledge and best practices to drive industry-wide sustainability improvements.

5. **Long-term commitment matters.** Sustainability in aviation is not a one-time effort but an ongoing commitment. SkyTeam already sees a future for the Sustainable Flight Challenge evolving into an independent industry initiative and involving various players in the aviation value chain.

CONCLUSION

AVIATION IS IN THE LAST CHANCE SALOON—HERE'S WHAT WE NEED TO DO NOW

IN JULY 2023, Norwegian climate advocate and investor Brita Staal was taking a flight out of Athens, Greece, where she had been for work.[1]

Her visit had coincided with the country facing record temperatures, causing wildfires.[2] On the popular tourist island of Rhodes those wildfires led to the emergency evacuation of 19,000 people,[3] in a situation one British holidaymaker described as "literally like the end of the world."[4]

Posted on *We Don't Have Time*, Staal's powerful and sobering account recounts her visit and flight home.[5]

Staal talked about "a walk of shame" in Athens, from where the wealthy were "drinking their frozen margaritas before noon" minutes away from dusty sidewalks where the homeless had little to no shelter from the searing heat.

On her return flight, "fleeing on a combustion engine giga-machine throwing out more of the problem that made us all get to this point," she described fellow passengers, "sighing and looking forward to the cold, fresh air of the North." According to Staal, even though everyone had been provided "front row seats to another climate disaster," their solution was to "sip [their] coffees and move on."[6]

In her piece, Staal concluded that climate emergencies like the one she experienced show that policymakers need to tax polluting industries like aviation, and they need to do it now.

Staal's account was written in 2023, with 27 years to go before the aviation industry is due to meet its net-zero target. Meanwhile, much of Europe, China,[7] and the United States also experienced record heat in 2023, with New York blanketed in smoke from Canadian wildfires. [8]

What kind of first-person accounts from the frontlines of the climate crisis will we be reading in 2033 or even 2043? What will attitudes to aviation be like then?

WIZARDS VERSUS PROPHETS

As we've shown in this book, the innovators working to decarbonise aviation have proposed solutions ranging from hydrogen-powered aircraft to fuels made out of thin air. There are airlines planting fuel crops in inhospitable desert conditions and others planning to fly electric aircraft connecting remote islands.

Their ingenuity, spirit of innovation, and dedication to slowing climate change, the defining problem of our time, are infectious. We believe in them, and it is a belief that makes us "wizards" as opposed to "prophets," terms first popularised by Charles C. Mann in his 2018 book *The Wizard and the Prophet: Two Views of the Future.*[9]

Prophets say there are environmental limits the planet can tolerate and that we've been more than exceeding them. Their emphasis is on reducing consumption, often combined with a reimagining society so that it no longer runs on capitalist principles, which they say are the root cause of humanity living beyond its ecological means.

By contrast, wizards believe that technological solutions, innovation, and human ingenuity can point the way forward. They say that we can enhance our quality of life with new technologies and to a non-fossil-fuel future. To take an example from this book, consider the electric aircraft makers who believe they can provide fast and clean transport for communities worldwide ill-served by existing infrastructure.

But the wizard perspective has been criticised as being at best naive and at worst a delay to the real changes that are needed.

In a paper published in July 2020 by Cambridge University Press, researchers outlined the different "discourses of climate delay."[10] One tactic identified by the authors was "technological optimism," where hopes were pinned on technologies that didn't yet exist at scale as a way of hindering real transformation.

The authors are aware of that possible criticism and want to address it directly. We don't only want to see discussion of new sustainable aviation technologies. We also want to see funding gaps bridged that will allow these technologies to be scaled and implemented.

Upon the release of the IPCC report in 2023, the UN Secretary-General Antonio Guteress said, "Now is the time to turn rage into action. Every fraction of a degree matters. Every voice can make a difference. And every second counts." [11]

To Guteress' point, we believe it is imperative that the aviation industry take action to reduce its climate impact—and not in 2050, but today. It is also imperative that travellers make conscious choices to reduce their carbon footprints every time they book a flight. And it is imperative that those of us with the most influence help lead the way for others. Here is how.

WE DARE THE AVIATION INDUSTRY TO

Based on all the conversations we have had while writing this book, we've put together eight crucial principles that we believe aviation must follow in order to reach net zero. They are as follows:

1. Tie growth to sustainability.
2. Combine incentives and mandates.
3. Apply the "polluter pays principle" as a Clean Skies Fund.
4. Focus on global equity, including the "Global South."
5. Ensure aviation doesn't take more than its fair share.
6. Emphasise transparency, accountability, and targets.
7. Encourage cooperation and knowledge sharing.
8. Ultimately aim for true-zero, not net-zero.

1. Tie growth to sustainability.

We do not believe that degrowth is the answer. Our aim is to ensure that the benefits of air travel continue for future generations, reaching even more people and particularly in regions where international travel remains a novelty.

Yet, we acknowledge the imperative of decoupling growth from emissions. Expansion should only occur if it aligns with sustainability goals.

Net-zero plans must encompass an overall reduction in airlines' carbon footprints, avoiding reliance solely on per passenger or per seat figures, which can be misleading. A practical step towards this goal is to tie new aeroplane orders explicitly to Sustainable Aviation Fuel (SAF), ensuring an immediate impact in the journey towards sustainability.

2. Combine incentives and mandates.

Recognising the industry's financial constraints, it's clear that the $4 trillion decarbonisation bill cannot be solely paid by the industry itself. The participation of both the private sector and governments is crucial.

To spur investments in net-zero technologies worldwide, we propose the implementation of incentives akin to the US Inflation Reduction Act.

These incentives should run in tandem with mandates that drive the industry away from reliance on fossil fuels. In this way, we can combine the "carrot" of incentives and the "stick" of mandates to create a powerful mechanism for change. As emphasised by ATAG's Haldane Dodd in the Introduction, mandates alone make little sense if there is no viable path to meet them. Hence, this balanced approach paves the way for effective and tangible progress.

3. Apply the "polluter pays" principle as a Clean Skies Fund.

The widely acknowledged "polluter pays" principle holds the appropriate, responsible parties accountable for their climate impact and its prevention. In aviation, we can apply this principle through two approaches.

First, while implementing carbon taxes on airlines, we should strike a balance between acknowledging aviation's environmental impact and ensuring fairness without jeopardising airlines' viability.

Second, we should explore contributions from those who fly the most. In our Introduction, we presented the ICCT's Frequent Flyer Levy proposal, which, if adopted industry-wide, could cover a substantial 80% of decarbonisation costs.

While we support the principle, we propose reframing it. Instead of labelling it as a tax or levy, we envision it as a "clean skies fund." This could take the form of a small surcharge on flight tickets, akin to fuel surcharges used in response to oil price fluctuations. The funds raised would be transparently invested in green technologies or pooled into a sustainability fund.

Notably, flights operated by aircraft featuring new technologies would be exempt from these charges, creating an additional incentive for the development of greener alternatives.

4. Focus on global equity, including the "Global South."

While much focus has been on aviation decarbonisation efforts in the so-called Global North, particularly in Europe and North America, it's essential to recognise that India holds the title of the world's largest aviation growth market.[12]

As a result, industry-wide decarbonisation means involving a wider range of countries than is currently the case.

One promising avenue is the development of SAF feedstocks indigenous to the Global South. For instance, the UAE and Etihad have supported SAF production from the resource-efficient Salicornia plant, as highlighted in Chapter 2.

Green hydrogen production also presents significant opportunities, as it can be used both in e-fuels and as a direct aircraft fuel source. Both the UAE and India are actively aiming to become green hydrogen hubs, with India targeting a production of 5 MMT (Million Metric Tonnes) per annum by 2030.[13]

Accelerating initiatives like these requires the support of Western investors and capital. The global nature of greenhouse gas emissions makes it evident that progress in the Global South will benefit everyone, regardless of their geographical location. Embracing these opportunities will pave the way for a more inclusive and effective approach to decarbonising aviation.

5. Ensure aviation doesn't take more than its fair share.

In our Introduction, we addressed environmental concerns about the resource intensity of aviation decarbonisation solutions. This includes the demand for land to cultivate fuel crops for SAF and the renewable resources required for e-fuels.

Given that aviation is just one among many industries striving for net-zero emissions, it must be conscious not to take more than its fair share. Investments should prioritise SAF pathways that consume less energy and resources. Additionally, it is important to explore more efficient approaches to green hydrogen development as well, such as by utilising next-generation electrolysers.

By making thoughtful choices about sustainable solutions, the aviation sector can play its part in the global push for net zero without undue strain on valuable resources.

6. Emphasise transparency, accountability, and targets.

In the past, the airline industry has faced accusations of making ambitious sustainability claims that were either delayed or quietly shelved.[14] This has resulted in an erosion of trust.

To regain that trust, airlines must prioritise practicality and feasibility in their net-zero roadmaps. Transparency is key, with sustainability programmes clearly outlining how airlines plan to achieve their goals and timelines.

To ensure accountability, independent third-party verification through organisations like SBTi should be encouraged. In this book, we've written about how both JetBlue and KLM have committed to adhering to SBTi principles, offering a model for building credibility.

7. Encourage industry cooperation and knowledge sharing.

In the Skyteam chapter, we highlighted how the alliance emphasised knowledge sharing and collaboration among airlines in order to achieve sustainability.

Another instance of cooperation can be seen in JetBlue and Hawaiian Airlines joining the United Airlines Sustainable Flight Fund.[15] This initiative allows organisations in the travel and aerospace sectors to pool their resources to invest in and purchase SAF.

The enormity of aviation's impact on the climate demands a unified effort, and no single player can tackle it alone. By combining capabilities and know-how, the industry can transcend isolated islands of effort. Collective power is the key to paving the way for a greener and more sustainable future for aviation.

8. The eventual goal should be true-zero, not net-zero.

In the medium term, SAF needs to be the primary decarbonisation solution, given that it works with the tens of thousands of aircraft flying today. Even so, emphasising the adoption of alternative fuels that yield maximum lifecycle CO_2 reduction, such as those being developed by Air Company, is imperative wherever possible.

In the long term, our vision is for electric and hydrogen-powered planes to be developed and utilised to their full potential. As highlighted by Val Miftakhov of ZeroAvia and Paul Eremenko of Universal Hydrogen, the use of these aircraft will usher in a true-zero future where aviation has next to no climate impact, steering us toward an environmentally-friendlier era of air travel.

THE ALTERNATIVE: THE EROSION OF AVIATION'S SOCIAL LICENSE

So, what happens if we don't accelerate the pace of decarbonisation? If we fail to take decisive steps, others will take charge. Policymakers will implement flight restrictions, responding to public demands for action against climate change's increasing impact on society.

In such a future, air travel will be perceived as a social ill, akin to alcohol or tobacco consumption, by segments of the public.

The many interviews we carried out for this book have shown that there is a way forward. However, we're also sitting in the last chance saloon. To get out of this situation, decarbonisation efforts have to be scaled up without delay.

But what about you? What can you do as an individual traveller?

AS A TRAVELLER, WE DARE YOU TO

For many people reading this book, aviation is likely the biggest portion of their personal carbon footprint, especially for frequent flyers. Even so, there are a number of things we can do to lower our individual carbon footprints while sending a message to the industry based on our travel habits.

They are as follows:

1. Consider the number of long-haul flights you take.
2. Combine trips and take work-ations.
3. Fly on new aircraft when you can.
4. Fly non-stop.
5. Offset with SAF or carbon capture where possible.
6. Take the train for shorter trips.
7. Be more sustainable when you fly.

1. Consider the number of long-haul flights you take.

When flying from London to New York, our carbon footprint at that moment becomes higher than the *annual* average for people in 56 countries.[16]

Unfortunately, long-haul flights are also the hardest to decarbonise; potential solutions like Heart Aerospace's electric aircraft will not address long-haul flights, and hydrogen solutions for long-haul travel are decades away.

As a result, if you're looking to dramatically reduce your own carbon footprint, think about the number of long-haul flights you take. Is your journey necessary? Could you combine any work and holiday trips?

2. Combine trips and take work-ations.

If you have to fly long-haul, why not combine a work trip

with a vacation? This has come to be known as blended travel, where the traditional boundaries of business and leisure are blurred.

There has been a significant rise in blended travel since the end of the pandemic, with more people taking longer trips to combine work and pleasure—and doing so can result in taking fewer trips per year.

3. Fly in a new aircraft when you can.

Modern aircraft are lighter since they're often made with composite materials and hence burn less fuel. They are also often equipped with newer engines that can be up to 20% more efficient than older models.

When booking a flight, look up what model aircraft you'll be flying on via your airline's website, or use a search tool like Google Flights that discloses the carbon footprint of your flight. Whenever possible, try to fly on newer aircraft.

4. Fly non-stop.

While multi-stop itineraries may yield more status miles in frequent flyer programs and are sometimes cheaper, most of them result in additional and avoidable emissions. In most cases, flying non-stop is less carbon intensive. Moreover, as much as 17% of a flight's fuel burn happens when it is taxiing for take-off, which is also limited by flying non-stop.[17]

5. Offset with SAF or carbon capture where possible.

On our *Sustainability in the Air* podcast, United Airlines CEO Scott Kirby said that it would be impossible to plant enough trees to offset all CO2 emissions caused by human activities.[18]

When you choose to offset your travels, consider flying on aircraft that use SAF to have the greatest impact—whether by indirectly reducing the emissions of a future flight or because the fuel was produced by taking CO2 out of the air via carbon capture.

6. Take the train for shorter trips.

In 2023, France banned flight routes between cities in cases where high-speed trains were available to take travellers there in less than 2.5 hours instead.[19]

In most cases, travelling by train results in fewer emissions than travelling by plane, so travellers should look for these options whenever possible. Airlines like KLM already offer train+plane itineraries, allowing travellers to travel to destinations half by train and half in the air to lower their total carbon emissions.

7. Be more sustainable when you fly.

Even if the best options aren't always available, travellers can still reduce their carbon footprint when they fly by doing the following:

- **Think about whether you need the in-flight meal** (and let the airline know ahead of time). Less food waste goes a long way, since the airline also gets to load less food.
- **Don't check bags.** Less weight carried means less fuel burned.
- **Take public transport to and from the airport.** Most major airports have good public transportation options to the city centre or beyond.
- **Stay in an eco-friendly hotel.** Many hotels today have an eco-rating on sites like Booking.com. Try to find out what sustainability efforts your hotel is pursuing to make your stay more sustainable.

In addition to all the above, there are still some of us who can do more than others to reduce aviation's climate impact. If this sounds like you, consider the following:

1. If you are a senior aviation executive...

Why not leave your settled job with the generous benefits and join a fledgling technology company that can help catalyse aviation's journey towards sustainability? As we've shown in this book, many new aviation technology companies were started by founders with little or no aviation experience.

Senior aviation executives can potentially make the biggest impact of their career by sharing their knowledge with new sustainability-oriented startups to help them scale. After all, what would be more fulfilling: taking a fifth annual flight to Orlando from Europe or working on technology that can potentially make travel greener?

2. If you can't leave your role yet...

We understand that many things need to fall in place to leave a position that has taken up most of one's life. Even so, those who can't leave their jobs can still make an impact by joining growth-stage sustainable aviation companies as advisors, board members, or even personal mentors to the founders. As we've seen, aviation executives often underestimate the value of their industry experience.

3. If you work in technology or with a large consulting company...

It's time to move on from products or roles that are squeezing out 0.1% operational efficiencies. Instead, start a project or lead a product that can help make an outsized impact of 10% or more than current technologies in aviation.

4. If you are an engineering student...

Work on technologies that aren't prevalent in the industry yet but have the potential to help aviation reach true zero rather than simply net zero. Since you have an entire career ahead of you, use it to work with companies that are shifting the landscape rather than simply trying to fit in and do more of the same.

5. If you are an aviation student...

Start a club or a society at your institution that explores sustainable options for travel. Do an internship with an organisation making big and bold bets on sustainability, be it JetBlue aiming for net zero by 2040 or SkyTeam encouraging a greener culture of aviation today.

When you graduate, don't automatically go for the most prestigious brand or the airline with the most travel benefits. Instead, find the sustainability innovator of your region and help them invent a future that benefits future generations in more ways than one.

6. If you are a politician...

Enact legislation that encourages the development of sustainable aviation. These measures can be mandates like those that already exist for SAF in the European Union or incentives like those found in the USA's Inflation Reduction Act. Each of these will help future generations travel in more sustainable ways—an impact that will go a long way in leaving a legacy that outlasts your term.

NOTES

WELCOME TO THE SILICON SKIES

1. Berlin, Leslie, https://leslieberlinauthor.com/.
2. Berlin, Leslie, "Recode Decode: Leslie Berlin, historian, Stanford University," *Decoder with Nilay Patel*, podcast audio, December 2017, https://open.spotify.com/episode/0nXy9CWrK4j8Ikvw65YOkr?si=OkFmKBpZTxS d1c1jof2m9w&nd=1.
3. Berlin, Leslie, *Troublemakers: Silicon Valley's Coming of Age* (Simon & Schuster, November 20, 2018).
4. "The Trillion-Dollar Opportunity in Climate Technology", *BCG*, January 10, 2023, https://www.bcg.com/news/10january2023-trillion-dollar-opportunity-in-climate-technology.
5. Liu, Coco, "What One of Climate Tech's Earliest Investors Thinks Is Coming Next", *Bloomberg*, July 5, 2023, https://www.bloomberg.com/news/articles/2023-07-05/climate-startup-investor-sean-o-sullivan-on-next-wave-of-tech-q-a.
6. "Swissport Sets Target for Minimum Share of 50% of Electric Vehicles in Its Global Fleet by 2025", *Swissport*, September 13, 2019, https://www.swissport.com/en/news/current-news/2019/swissport-sets-target-for-minimum-share-of-50-of-electric-vehicles-in-its-global-fleet-by-2025.
7. "Airport City Solar" YEG Edmonton International Airport, September 13, 2019, https://flyeia.com/corporate/esg/environmental-sustainability/airport-city-solar/.
8. "Aviation Sector Starts Follow-up Sustainable Taxiing Tests at Schiphol", Schiphol, December 7, 2022, https://news.schiphol.com/aviation-sector-starts-follow-up-sustainable-taxiing-tests-at-schiphol/.
9. Blanshard, Alastair, "Fueling Net Zero: Sustainable Pathways for Aviation", ICF, March 8, 2022, https://www.icf.com/insights/transportation/fueling-net-zero-sustainable-pathways-for-aviation.
10. "More than One Quarter of All Venture Capital Funding Is Going to Climate Technology, with Increased Focus on Technologies that Have the Most Potential to Cut Emissions", *PWC*, March 11, 2022, https://www.pwc.com/gx/en/news-room/press-releases/2022/state-of-climate-tech-report-2022.html.
11. "Investing in Climate Tech: An Opportunity for Europe", *World Fund*, https://www.worldfund.vc/wp/investments-in-climate-tech.
12. "Decarbonising the Energy System by 2050 Could save Trillions - Oxford Study", University of Oxford, September 14, 2022, https://www.ox.ac.uk/news/2022-09-14-decarbonising-energy-system-2050-could-save-trillions-oxford-study.

13. Callaway, David, "Decarbonising the Energy System by 2050 Could save Trillions - Oxford Study", *Callaway Climate Insights*, March 17, 2020, https://www.callawayclimateinsights.com/p/zeus-the-coming-battle-with-the-climate.

AVIATION'S EXISTENTIAL PROBLEM

1. ABC News, "Several passengers hospitalized after extreme turbulence, emergency landing | GMA", *Good Morning America*, video, https://www.youtube.com/watch?v=xT5gzgIOSlY.
2. Williams, Paul, "Severe clear-air turbulence...", LinkedIn blog post, June 2023, https://www.linkedin.com/posts/pauldavidwilliams_severe-clear-air-turbulence-over-the-north-activity-7072565280941428736-g7fQ.
3. Prosser, Mark C.; Williams, Paul D.; Marlton, Graeme J.; and Harrison, R. G., "Evidence for Large Increases in Clear-Air Turbulence Over the Past Four Decades", *Geophysical Research Letters 50*, no. 11 (2023), https://agupubs.onlinelibrary.wiley.com/doi/10.1029/2023GL103814#pane-pcw-references.
4. Chow, Denise, "Carbon Dioxide Hits a Level Not Seen for 3 Million Years. Here's what that Means for Climate Change — And Humanity.", *NBC News*, May 14, 2019, https://www.nbcnews.com/mach/science/carbon-dioxide-hits-level-not-seen-3-million-years-here-ncna1005231.
5. Kommenda, Niko, "How Your Flight Emits as Much CO2 as Many People Do in a Year", *The Guardian*, July 19, 2019, https://www.theguardian.com/environment/ng-interactive/2019/jul/19/carbon-calculator-how-taking-one-flight-emits-as-much-as-many-people-do-in-a-year.
6. Ritchie, Hannah and Roser, Max, "Transport", *Our World in Data*, Y Combinator, September 1, 2021, https://ourworldindata.org/transport.
7. "World Air Passenger Traffic Evolution, 1980-2020", IEA, December 3, 2020, https://www.iea.org/data-and-statistics/charts/world-air-passenger-traffic-evolution-1980-2020.
8. "2050 Air Traffic Forecast Showing Aviation Pathway to Net-zero", *Eurocontrol*, April 13, 2022, https://www.eurocontrol.int/press-release/eurocontrol-2050-air-traffic-forecast-showing-aviation-pathway-net-zero.
9. IATA, "Global Outlook for Air Transport: Sustained Recovery Amidst Strong Headwinds," December 2022, https://www.iata.org/en/iata-repository/publications/economic-reports/global-outlook-for-air-transport---december-2022/.
10. Vigeveno, Huibert, "Aviation's Flight Path to a Net-zero Future", *World Economic Forum*, September 20, 2021, https://www.weforum.org/agenda/2021/09/aviation-flight-path-to-net-zero-future/.
11. Jaramillo, Paulina, Suzana K. Ribiero, Newman, Peter et al, "IPCC Sixth Assessment Report, Transport", Intergovernmental Panel on Climate Change (IPCC), March 20, 2023, https://www.ipcc.ch/report/ar6/wg3/downloads/report/IPCC_AR6_WGIII_Chapter10.pdf.
12. "#SayYesToTheWorld."
    Lufthansa, https://www.lufthansa.com/si/en/benefits.

13. Frost, Rosie, "In Pictures: Activists Take over Billboards to Call Out Impact of Flying on Global Carbon Emissions", *Euronews Green*, September 22, 2022, https://www.euronews.com/green/2022/09/22/activists-take-over-billboards-to-call-out-impact-of-flying-on-global-carbon-emissions.

14. Subvertisers International (@SubvertisersInt), ""a closer look reveals cheeky phrases" Our Europe-wide subvertising campaign with @BrandalismUK brings "focus not only to the problem of wasteful air travel, but the advertising that props them up" - via @hyperallergic", Twitter, September 27, 2022, https://twitter.com/SubvertisersInt/status/1574713203371560960.

15. Brandalism (@BrandalismUK), "Time to stop airline adverts fuelling the climate emergency. Support the European Citizens Initiative to #BanFossilAds at https://banfossilfuelads.org", Twitter, September 23, 2022, https://twitter.com/BrandalismUK/status/1573270985800826882.

16. "353,103 People Have Taken Action to Call for a European Ban of Fossil Fuel Advertising and Sponsorships", *Ban Fossil Fuel Ads*, September 22, 2022, https://banfossilfuelads.org/.

17. "Earth Day 2022: Global Attitudes to Climate Change", *Ipsos*, April 18, 2022, https://www.ipsos.com/en-us/news-polls/global-advisor-earth-day-2022.

18. "Fewer Consumers Say They Have Changed Their Behavior Due to Climate Concern than Did before the Pandemic", *Ipsos*, November 3, 2021, https://www.ipsos.com/en-us/news-polls/climate-change-consumer-behavior-2021.

19. Carroll, Sean G., "Business as Usual 'Dangerous' for Aviation, Warns Rome Airport Chief", *Euractiv*, February 20, 2023, https://www.euractiv.com/section/aviation/news/business-as-usual-dangerous-for-aviation-warns-rome-airport-chief/.

20. "The Aerospace & Defense Showcase", Deep-Tech Showcase, January 26, 2023, https://www.deeptechshowcase.com/aerospace-defense-showcase-2023/.

21. Futures Centre, "Norway Plans to Make All Short-haul Flights Electric by 2040", *Forum for the Future*, April 4, 2023,/https://www.thefuturescentre.org/signal/norway-plans-to-make-all-short-haul-flights-electric-by-2040/.

22. "Denmark to Make Domestic Flights Fossil Fuel Free by 2030", *BBC News*, January 2, 2022, https://www.bbc.com/news/world-europe-59849898.

23. Bryant, Mike, "Dutch Government to Appeal against Court'S Ruling on Schiphol Flights", *Air Cargo News*, April 13, 2023, https://www.bbc.com/news/world-europe-59849898.

24. Singh, Sumit, "Belgium To Introduce New Taxes On Short-Haul Flights & Private Jets", *Simple Flying*, December 10, 2022, https://simpleflying.com/new-taxes-short-haul-flights-private-jets/.

25. Limb, Lottie, "It's Official: France Bans Short-haul Domestic Flights in Favour of Train Travel", *Euronews Green*, February 12, 2022, https://www.euronews.com/green/2022/12/02/is-france-banning-private-jets-everything-we-know-from-a-week-of-green-transport-proposals.

26. Smith, Ian, "France Is Raising Taxes on Flights to Pay for Trains: Should Other European Countries Do the Same?", *Euronews Green*, October 8, 2023,

https://www.euronews.com/green/2023/08/10/france-is-raising-taxes-on-flights-to-pay-for-trains-should-other-european-countries-do-th.

27. "States Adopt Net-zero 2050 Global Aspirational Goal for International Flight Operations", International Civil Aviation Organization (ICAO), October 7, 2022, https://www.icao.int/Newsroom/Pages/States-adopts-netzero-2050-aspirational-goal-for-international-flight-operations.aspx.

28. Mithal, Shraeya and Rutherford, Dan, "ICAO'S 2050 Net-Zero CO2 Goal for International Aviation", International Council on Clean Transportation (ICCT), January 5, 2023, https://theicct.org/publication/global-aviation-icao-net-zero-goal-jan23/.

29. Graver, Brandon PhD, Zheng, Xinya S., Rutherford PhD, Daniel et al, "Vision 2050: Aligning Aviation with the Paris Agreement," International Council on Clean Transportation (ICCT), June 2022, https://theicct.org/wp-content/uploads/2022/06/Aviation-2050-Report-A4-v6.pdf.

30. Ibid.

31. Hancock, Alice, Georgiadis, Philip and Hodgson, Camilla, "Airline Passengers Face Higher Fares under New EU Emissions Rules, *Financial Times*, February 13, 2023, https://www.ft.com/content/3b81be27-09ee-4251-8dda-22a2d7ea7479.

32. "A321neo: The Most Successful Commercial Aircraft Family Ever", Airbus Aircraft, February 13, 2023, https://aircraft.airbus.com/en/aircraft/a320-the-most-successful-aircraft-family-ever/a321neo.

33. Singer, Dirk, "Can Aviation Growth Be Reconciled with Decarbonisation? An Industry Panel Takes Stock", *Sustainability in the Air*, Simpli Flying, May 2, 2023, https://green.simpliflying.com/p/can-aviation-growth-be-reconciled.

34. Gill, Rob, "EU Agrees Deal on Mandate for Sustainable Aviation Fuel", *Business Travel News Europe*, April 26, 2023, https://www.businesstravelnewseurope.com/Air-Travel/EU-agrees-deal-on-mandate-for-sustainable-aviation-fuel.

35. "EU Agrees to World's Largest Green Fuels Mandate for Aviation", *Transport & Environment*, April 26, 2023, https://www.transportenvironment.org/discover/eu-agrees-to-worlds-largest-green-fuels-mandate-for-aviation/.

36. "FACT SHEET: Biden Administration Advances the Future of Sustainable Fuels in American Aviation", The White House, September 9, 2021, https://www.whitehouse.gov/briefing-room/statements-releases/2021/09/09/fact-sheet-biden-administration-advances-the-future-of-sustainable-fuels-in-american-aviation/.

37. Frangoul, Anmar, "Sustainable Aviation Fuel Costs More but Consumers Will Be Willing to Pay, IATA Chief Says," *CNBC*, February 11, 2022, https://www.cnbc.com/2022/02/11/sustainable-aviation-fuel-costs-more-but-consumers-willing-to-pay-iata.html.

38. Goldstein, Michael, "Sustainable Jet Fuel Costs 8X Regular Fuel; Can Oil Giants Scale Up Production By 2025 To Cut Carbon?", *Forbes*, September 23, 2021, https://www.forbes.com/sites/michaelgoldstein/2021/09/23/can-oil-industry-giants-like-shell-provide-sustainable-jet-fuel-by-2025/?sh=5f6f92ec3e00.

39. Carey, Bill, "Enthusiasm For Sustainable Aviation Fuel Meets Supply Reality", *Aviation Week Network*, December 20, 2022, https://aviationweek.com/

aerospace/emerging-technologies/enthusiasm-sustainable-aviation-fuel-meets-supply-reality.

40. "Clean Skies for Tomorrow Sustainable Aviation Fuels as a Pathway to Net-Zero Aviation", World Economic Forum and McKinsey & Company, November 2022, https://www3.weforum.org/docs/WEF_Clean_Skies_To morrow_SAF_Analytics_2020.pdf.

41. "Get Information: How Unjust Is Flying?", *Stay Grounded*, December 20, 2022, https://stay-grounded.org/get-information/.

42. Becken, Susanne, Mackey, Brendan and Lee, David S., "Implications of Preferential Access to Land and Clean Energy for Sustainable Aviation Fuels", *Science of The Total Environment 886*, May 8, 2023, https://www.sciencedirect.com/science/article/pii/S0048969723025044.

43. Douglas, Craig and James, Ben, "Electrofuels for Aviation", *World Fund*, December 1, 2022, https://www.worldfund.vc/knowledge/electrofuels-for-aviation.

44. McEwan, Alasdair, "Is there any hope for a green aviation industry?", September 23, 2022, *Land & Climate Review*, interview with Finlay Asher, podcast, https://www.buzzsprout.com/1695859/11372779.

45. https://safe-landing.org/.

46. "Tax Frequent Fliers to Decarbonize Aviation Fairly, Study Urges", International Council on Clean Transportation (ICCT), September 28, 2022, https://theicct.org/freq-flier-aviation-pr-sep22/.

47. "Solar Panels and the White House", *Science Museum*, June 20, 2018, https://blog.sciencemuseum.org.uk/solar-panels-and-the-white-house/.

48. "Evolution of Solar PV Module Cost by Data Source, 1970-2020", IEA, July 2, 2020, https://www.iea.org/data-and-statistics/charts/evolution-of-solar-pv-module-cost-by-data-source-1970-2020.

49. Evans, Simon, "Solar Is now 'Cheapest Electricity in History', Confirms IEA", *Carbon Brief*, October 13, 2020, https://www.carbonbrief.org/solar-is-now-cheapest-electricity-in-history-confirms-iea/.

50. "Electric Pioneer Velis Electro," Pipistrel, https://www.pipistrel-aircraft.com/products/velis-electro/.

51. Donofrio, Joel, "Electric Aircraft Could Make Yakima an Expansion Option, Airport Official Says", *The Seattle Times*, April 24, 2023, https://www.seattletimes.com/business/boeing-aerospace/electric-aircraft-could-make-yakima-an-expansion-option-airport-official-says/.

52. Read more about EP Power Systems in Chapter 3.

53. "New Podcast Episode, Aircraft Batteries with Richard Wang (Cuberg)," *Allplane*, May 21, 2023, https://allplane.tv/blog/2023/5/20/new-podcast-episode-aircraft-batteries-richard-wang-cuberg.

54. Bleakley, Daniel, "World's Largest Battery Maker Announces Major Breakthrough in Energy Density", *The Driven*, April 21, 2023, https://thedriven.io/2023/04/21/worlds-largest-battery-maker-announces-major-breakthrough-in-battery-density/.

55. "The All-New Amprius 500 Wh/Kg Battery Platform Is Here," Amprius, March 23, 2023, https://amprius.com/the-all-new-amprius-500-wh-kg-battery-platform-is-here/.

56. "Powering a Safer World", Electric Power Systems, https://epsenergy.com/.

57. Singer, Dirk, "Cosmic Aerospace Aims to Make 1000 Km Electric Flight a Reality," *Sustainability in the Air*, May 25, 2023, https://green.simpliflying.com/p/cosmic-aerospace-aims-to-make-1000.

58. "ZEROe: Towards the World'S First Hydrogen-powered Commercial Aircraft," Airbus, https://www.airbus.com/en/innovation/low-carbon-aviation/hydrogen/zeroe.

59. Read more about ZeroAvia in Chapter 7.

60. Read more about Universal Hydrogen in Chapter 3

61. "Analysing the Future Cost of Green Hydrogen," *PwC*, https://www.pwc.com/gx/en/issues/esg/the-energy-transition/analysing-future-cost-of-green-hydrogen.html.

62. Gençer, Emre, "Hydrogen", *MIT Climate Portal*, June 23, 2021, https://climate.mit.edu/explainers/hydrogen.

63. "Green Hydrogen," *Sungreen*, https://www.sungreenh2.com/.

64. Collins, Leigh, "'World's Cheapest Green Hydrogen' | Start-up with Ultra-efficient Electrolyser to Develop Pilot Factory after Securing $29m", *Recharge News*, August 2, 2022, https://www.rechargenews.com/energy-transition/worlds-cheapest-green-hydrogen-start-up-with-ultra-efficient-electrolyser-to-develop-pilot-factory-after-securing-29m/2-1-1270403.https://www.rechargenews.com/energy-transition/worlds-cheapest-green-hydrogen-start-up-with-ultra-efficient-electrolyser-to-develop-pilot-factory-after-securing-29m/2-1-1270403.

65. Read more about Air Company in Chapter 6.

66. "Sustainable Aviation Fuel (SAF) Tax Credit", US Department of Energy - Alternative Fuels Data Center, https://afdc.energy.gov/laws/13160.

67. Mwangi, George, "Sustainable Aviation: California and Washington's Governors Highlight Progress So Far", *AeroXplorer*, May 11, 2023, https://aeroxplorer.com/articles/sustainable-aviation-california-and-washingtons-governors-highlight-progress-so-far.php.

68. Hussein, Sarfaraz, "The SAF Grand Challenge: Demand, Mandates and Incentives in California for Decarbonization of Aviation", *CCarbon*, February 15, 2023, https://www.ccarbon.info/the-saf-grand-challenge-demand-mandates-and-incentives-in-california-for-decarbonization-of-aviation/.

69. Keating, Dave, "Aviation Emissions: 'We Can't Wait for Hydrogen or Electric'", *Energy Monitor*, October 11, 2021, https://www.energymonitor.ai/sectors/transport/aviation-emissions-we-cant-wait-for-hydrogen-or-electric/.

70. Nigam, Shashank, "How Amex GBT is building platforms for SAF and Carbon Offsets", October 26, 2022, *Sustainability in the Air*, interview with Nora Lovell Merchant, podcast, https://green.simpliflying.com/p/nora-lovell-marchant-amex-gbt#details.

71. Grantham-Philips, Wyatte, "'Outrageous': Big Oil Made Almost $200 Billion in 2022 as World Faced Energy Crisis. Here's the Breakdown.", *USA Today*, February 10, 2023, https://www.usatoday.com/story/money/at-home/2023/02/10/oil-companies-2022-profits-exxon-bp-shell/11170023002/.

1. HEART AEROSPACE: HOW A HUSBAND-AND-WIFE TEAM PIONEERED ELECTRIC AIRCRAFT IN SWEDEN BY REIMAGINING REGIONAL AVIATION

1. Alter, Charlotte, Haynes, Syuin, and Worland, Justin, "Time 2019 Person of the Year: Greta Thunberg", *Time*, December 11, 2019, https://time.com/person-of-the-year-2019-greta-thunberg/.
2. Thunberg, Greta (@GretaThunberg), "Last month domestic air travel in Sweden was down 11%. In Germany it was down 12%. The climate- and environmental crisis can of course only be solved by a system change. But these numbers surely do help with bringing that change a little closer...", December 20, 2019, https://twitter.com/GretaThunberg/status/1208080233754181634.
3. "The inside Story of Greta Thunberg's Upwind Atlantic Crossing on La Vagabonde", *Yachting World*, February 13, 2020, https://www.yachtingworld.com/sailing-across-atlantic/greta-thunberg-atlantic-crossing-la-vagabonde-125068.
4. "Heart Aerospace Hangar Day 2022 Full Presentation", Heart Aerospace, September 21, 2022, video, https://www.youtube.com/watch?v=h87i1wwX3R8.
5. "When Will Commercial Electric Aircraft Become a Reality?", Aviation Benefits Beyond Borders, https://aviationbenefits.org/faqs/electric-aircraft/.
6. Dixon, Chris, "Do You Want to Sell Sugar Water or Do You Want to Change the World?", *Business Insider*, August 28, 2011, https://www.businessinsider.com/do-you-want-to-sell-sugar-water-or-do-you-want-to-change-the-world-2011-9?r=US&IR=T.
7. https://www.youtube.com/watch?v=IwOfCgkyEj0.
8. "Seed Round - Heart Aerospace", *Crunchbase*, https://www.crunchbase.com/funding_round/heart-aerospace-seed--72abc28c.
9. https://www.hbo.com/silicon-valley.
10. "Chris Sacca", *Forbes*, April 6, 2021, https://www.forbes.com/profile/chris-sacca/?sh=5de97851220a.
11. "ETL Speaker Series: Chris Sacca, Lowercarbon Capital", Stanford eCorner, February 16, 2022, video, https://youtu.be/ZMJa231UfwY.
12. Nigam, Shashank, "Why Heart Aerospace's electric aircraft is a gamechanger", October 6, 2022, *Sustainability in the Air*, interview with Anders Forslund, podcast, https://green.simpliflying.com/p/anders-forslund-ceo-heart-aerospaces#details.
13. Heart Aerospace, "BAE Systems and Heart Aerospace to Collaborate on Battery for Electric Airplane", *PR Newswire*, March 30, 2023, https://www.prnewswire.com/news-releases/bae-systems-and-heart-aerospace-to-collaborate-on-battery-for-electric-airplane-301784986.html.
14. Mukhopadhaya, Jayant and Graver, Brandon. "Performance Analysis of Regional Electric Aircraft", *International Council on Clean Transportation (ICCT)*, July 13, 2022, https://theicct.org/publication/global-aviation-performance-analysis-regional-electric-aircraft-jul22/.

15. "SABERS: Solid-state Architecture Batteris for Enhanced Rechargeability and Safety", NASA, July 13, 2022, https://www.nasa.gov/sites/default/files/atoms/files/sabers_cas_fact_sheet_508.pdf.
16. "NASA'S Solid-State Battery Research Exceeds Initial Goals, Draws Interest", NASA, October 7, 2022, https://www.nasa.gov/aeroresearch/nasa-solid-state-battery-research-exceeds-initial-goals-draws-interest.
17. De la Garza, Alejandro, "Forget Electric Cars, The Future of Battery Technology Is in Airplanes", *Time*, September 23, 2022, https://time.com/6236597/battery-technology-airplanes-richard-wang/.
18. Perry, Dominic, "Heart Taps BAE Systems for ES-30 Battery Work", *FlightGlobal*, March 30, 2023, https://www.flightglobal.com/air-transport/heart-taps-bae-systems-for-es-30-battery-work/152676.article.
19. "Mesa to Invest in Heart Aerospace and Orders 100 All-Electric Aircraft", *Mesa Air Group*, July 12, 2021, https://investor.mesa-air.com/news-releases/news-release-details/mesa-invest-heart-aerospace-and-orders-100-all-electric-aircraft.
20. "ICAO Carbon Emissions Calculator", International Civil Aviation Organisation (ICAO), https://www.icao.int/environmental-protection/Carbonoffset/Pages/default.aspx.
21. Singer, Dirk, "In Conversation: Air New Zealand CEO Greg Foran", *Apex*, October 27, 2022, https://apex.aero/articles/airnewzealand-greg-foran/.
22. "Heart Aerospace Unveils New Airplane Design, Confirms Air Canada and Saab as New Shareholders", *Heart Aerospace*, September 15, 2022, http://heartaerospace.com/heart-aerospace-unveils-new-airplane-design-confirms-air-canada-and-saab-as-new-shareholders/.
23. "Heart Aerospace Selected as Long-term Partner for Air New Zealand'S Mission Next Gen Aircraft", *Heart Aerospace*, February 7, 2023, /https://heartaerospace.com/newsroom/heart-aerospace-selected-as-long-term-partner-for-air-new-zealands-mission-next-gen-aircraft/.

2. ZEROAVIA: HYDROGEN-ELECTRIC ENGINES AND BUILDING A "CITY OF AVIATION" TO ENABLE A TRUE-ZERO FUTURE

1. "Enel Acquires EMotorWerks to Provide Grid Balancing Solutions and Tap into US E-mobility Market", *Enel X Way*, October 25, 2017, https://evcharging.enelx.com/news/releases/377-enel-acquires-emotorwerks.
2. For a longer explanation on why some companies choose to start from scratch, read Chapters 5 and 8, about Heart Aerospace and Archer Aviation, respectively.
3. Singer, Dirk, "Wisk Aims to Make Air Taxis as Affordable as an Uber X", *SimpliFlying*, July 20, 2022, https://simpliflying.com/blog/wisk-aims-to-make-air-taxis-as-affordable-as-an-uber-x/.
4. Badola, Ayushi, "Can Boom Bring Supersonics Back Sustainably?", *Sustainability in the Air*, September 22, 2022, https://green.simpliflying.com/p/blake-scholl-ceo-boom-supersonic#details.
5. "ZEROe", *Airbus*, September 22, 2022, https://www.airbus.com/en/innovation/zero-emission-journey/hydrogen/zeroe.

6. "Airline Contrails Warm the Planet Twice as Much as CO2, EU Study Finds", *Transport & Environment*, September 24, 2020, https://www.transportenviron ment.org/discover/airline-contrails-warm-planet-twice-much-co2-eu-study-finds/.
7. "Why Breakthrough Energy Is Excited about ZeroAvia", ZeroAvia, August 26, 2022, video, https://www.youtube.com/watch?v=ndKmvcH4xGk.
8. Ibid.
9. "Amazon Invests in ZeroAvia to Support the Development of Sustainable Aviation", Amazon, December 16, 2020, https://www.aboutamazon.com/ news/sustainability/amazon-invests-in-zeroavia-to-support-the-develop ment-of-sustainable-aviation.
10. "ZeroAvia Secures Additional $30 Million in Funding from IAG, Barclays, NEOM & AENU", *PR Newswire*, July 20, 2022. https://www.prnewswire. com/news-releases/zeroavia-secures-additional-30-million-in-funding-from-iag-barclays-neom--aenu-301589776.html.
11. "American Airlines Announces Investment in Hydrogen-Electric Engine Developer ZeroAvia", *ZeroAvia*, August 3, 2022, https://zeroavia.com/aa-investment/.
12. "Why Breakthrough Energy Is Excited about ZeroAvia", *ZeroAvia*, August 26, 2022, video, https://www.youtube.com/watch?v=ndKmvcH4xGk.
13. "ZeroAvia Completes World First Hydrogen-Electric Passenger Plane Flight", *PR Newswire*, September 24, 2020, https://www.prnewswire.com/news-releases/zeroavia-completes-world-first-hydrogen-electric-passenger-plane-flight-301137976.html.
14. "ZeroAvia Crash Investigation Complete: It Wasn't the Hydrogen", *New Atlas*, July 11, 2022, https://newatlas.com/aircraft/zeroavia-hydrogen-crash-investigation-report/.
15. Nehls, Grace, "ZeroAvia Receives CAA Approval for Next Phase of Hydro-gen-electric Test Flights", *Composites World*, January 3, 2023, https://www.-compositesworld.com/news/zeroavia-receives-caa-approval-for-next-phase-of-hydrogen-electric-test-flights.
16. "TPE331 Turboprop Engine", *Honeywell Aerospace*, January 3, 2023, https://aerospace.honeywell.com/us/en/products-and-services/product/hard ware-and-systems/engines/tpe331-turboprop-engine.
17. "De Havilland Canada Aircraft", *De Havilland Aircraft of Canada Limited*, January 3, 2023, https://dehavilland.com/en.
18. Hardee, Howard, "Alaska Airlines, ZeroAvia to Develop 'World'S Largest' Zero-emission Aircraft", Flight Global, May 1, 2023, https://www.flight global.com/safety/alaska-airlines-zeroavia-to-develop-worlds-largest-zero-emission-aircraft/153080.article.
19. Hardee, Howard, "ZeroAvia Finds Retrofitting CRJs with Hydrogen-electric Technology Feasible", *Flight Global*, June 19, 2023, https://www.flightglobal. com/air-transport/zeroavia-finds-retrofitting-crjs-with-hydrogen-electric-technology-feasible/153780.article.
20. Hardee, Howard, "ZeroAvia High Temperature Fuel Cell Testing Shows Large Aircraft and Rotorcraft Potential for Hydrogen-Electric Propulsion", *PR Newswire*, March 9, 2023, https://www.prnewswire.com/news-releases/

zeroavia-high-temperature-fuel-cell-testing-shows-large-aircraft-and-rotor craft-potential-for-hydrogen-electric-propulsion-301768084.html.

21. Niehls, Grace, "ZeroAvia, ZEV Station Gear up Hydrogen Refueling Ecosystem at California Airports", *Composites World*, April 6, 2022, https://www.compositesworld.com/news/zeroavia-zev-station-gear-up-hydrogen-refueling-ecosystem-at-california-airports.

22. "ZeroAvia & Edmonton International Airport Tie Up to Bring Hydrogen-Electric Flights to Canada", *ZeroAvia*, July 21, 2022, https://www.zeroavia.com/eia-collaboration.

23. Ahlgren, Linnea, "ZeroAvia Wants To Bring Zero-Emission Flights To Scotland", *Simple Flying*, September 2, 2022, https://simpleflying.com/zeroavia-zero-emissions-flights-scotland/.

24. Singer, Dirk, "Can Aviation Ever Be 'Clean'? Four Industry Insiders Give Their View", Sustainability in the Air, March 17, 2023, https://green.simpliflying.com/can-aviation-ever-be-clean-four-industry-insiders-give-their-view/.

25. "NEOM Airlines Set for Take-off by End of 2024, CEO Reveals", Arab News, March 24, 2023, https://www.arabnews.com/node/2274851/business-economy.

26. "The Red Sea Development Company Selects ZeroAvia to Develop Zero-Emission Flights for Luxury Destination", *ZeroAvia*, July 21, 2022, https://www.zeroavia.com/trsdc-partnership.

3. AIR COMPANY: FROM SCALING CARBON CAPTURE TECH WITH VODKA TO MAKING JET FUEL FROM THIN AIR

1. "Air Company's Gregory Constantine Joins GaryVee on #MarketingForTheNow Episode #18!", *VaynerMedia*, March 4, 2021, video, https://www.youtube.com/watch?v=b72nHD5SU4M.

2. "Thanksgiving Flashback: Air Company--Greg Constantine," *Climate Tech Cocktails*, September 23, 2022,https://www.climatetechcocktails.com/p/thanksgiving-flashback-air-company.

3. "Staff Sheehan," *Forbes*, September 23, 2022, https://www.forbes.com/profile/staff-sheehan/?sh=68538f114feb.

4. "Gregory Constantine," *Forbes*, September 23, 2022, https://www.forbes.com/profile/gregory-constantine/?sh=2039f8913c78.

5. "Forbes 2017 Under 30 Summit EMEA Will Conclude with Wide-Ranging Service Day on April 5, 2017", *Forbes*, March 19, 2017, https://www.forbes.com/sites/forbespr/2017/03/19/forbes-2017-under-30-summit-emea-will-conclude-with-wide-ranging-service-day-on-april-5-2017/?sh=3d786108676c.

6. "H&M Move Partners with LanzaTech to Launch Capsule Collection Using Captured Carbon Emissions", *LanzaTech*, April 6, 2023, https://lanzatech.com/hm-move-partners-with-lanzatech-to-launch-capsule-collection-using-captured-carbon-emissions/.

7. "World-first Laundry Capsule in Market Made from Industrial Carbon Emissions", *Unilever*, April 21, 2021, https://www.unilever.com/news/press-

and-media/press-releases/2021/world-first-laundry-capsule-in-market-made-from-industrial-carbon-emissions/.

8. Flavelle, Christopher, "Vodka From Thin Air: An Unusual Climate Prize Hits a Coronavirus Snag", *The New York Times*, March 30, 2020, https://www.nytimes.com/2020/03/30/climate/xprize-carbon-coronavirus.html.

9. Peters, Adele, "This Carbon-negative Vodka Is Made from Captured CO2", *Fast Company*, November 7, 2019, https://www.fastcompany.com/90422270/this-carbon-negative-vodka-is-made-from-captured-co2.

10. Waddoups, Ryan, "Behold, the First-Ever Fragrance Made From Air", *Surface Mag*, October 21, 2021, https://www.surfacemag.com/articles/air-company-perfumefragrance/.

11. "Vodka, Out of Thin Air", *Time*, September 19, 2020, https://time.com/collection/best-inventions-2020/5911376/air-vodka/.

12. "Vodka Made of CO₂ - Air Company", *XPrize*, https://www.xprize.org/prizes/carbon/product/vodka-made-of-co2.

13. "Air Company", *XPrize*, https://www.xprize.org/prizes/carbon/teams/air_company.

14. "STMD: Centennial Challenges", *NASA*, September 19, 2020, https://www.nasa.gov/directorates/spacetech/centennial_challenges/co2challenge/index.html.

15. "NASA CO2 Conversion Challenge Competitor Pitches in to Help COVID-19 Efforts", *NASA*, April 9, 2020, https://www.nasa.gov/directorates/spacetech/centennial_challenges/co2-conversion-challenge-competitor-pitches-in-to-help-covid-19-efforts.html.

16. "NASA Awards $750,000 in Competition to Convert Carbon Dioxide into Sugar", *NASA*, August 24, 2021, https://www.nasa.gov/directorates/spacetech/centennial_challenges/75K-awarded-in-competition-to-convert-carbon-dioxide-into-sugar.html.

17. "NASA's Project SABERS Is Testing a Graphene Battery that Could Be a Game Changer for Aviation and EVs", *Graphene Info*, December 13, 2022, https://www.graphene-info.com/nasas-project-sabers-testing-graphene-battery-could-be-game-changer-aviation.

18. "NASA Issues Award for Greener, More Fuel-Efficient Airliner of Future", *NASA*, January 18, 2023, https://www.nasa.gov/press-release/nasa-issues-award-for-greener-more-fuel-efficient-airliner-of-future.

19. Aziz, Afdhel, "From Vodka To Space Flight: Air Company Launches Sustainable Rocket Fuel To Help Us Get To Mars...And Beyond", *Forbes*, October 27, 2020, https://www.forbes.com/sites/afdhelaziz/2020/10/27/from-vodka-to-space-flight-air-co-launches-sustainable-rocket-fuel-to-help-us-get-to-marsand-beyond/?sh=533b51f22e4c.

20. Gorman, Steve, "NASA Looks to Spice up Astronaut Menu with Deep Space Food Production", *Reuters*, May 29, 2023, https://www.reuters.com/technology/space/nasa-looks-spice-up-astronaut-menu-with-deep-space-food-production-2023-05-29/.

21. Maj. Pearl, Nicole, Dr. Wrzesinski, Paul, and Capt. Mitchell, Kaleb, "Project FIERCE Fuels the Future of Synthetic Jet Fuel Generation", *Air Force Research Laboratory (AFRL)*, November 8, 2022, https://www.afrl.af.mil/News/Arti

cle-Display/Article/3189327/project-fierce-fuels-the-future-of-synthetic-jet-fuel-generation/.

22. Air Company, "Air Company Secures $30MM in Series A Funding to Further Scale Its Carbon Conversion Technology", *PR Newswire*, April 19, 2022, https://www.prnewswire.com/news-releases/air-company-secures-30mm-in-series-a-funding-to-further-scale-its-carbon-conversion-technology-301528300.html.

23. "Carbon Direct Capital - Investments", *Carbon Direct*, https://www.carbondirectcapital.com/#investments.

24. Gallucci, Maria, "CO2-to-vodka Startup Air Company Aims Higher with Aviation Fuel", *Canary Media*, September 22, 2022, https://www.canarymedia.com/articles/air-travel/co2-to-vodka-startup-air-company-aims-higher-with-aviation-fuel.

25. "Food Not Fuel: Why Biofuels Are a Risk to Food Security", *Transport & Environment*, March 24, 2022, https://www.transportenvironment.org/discover/food-not-fuel-why-biofuels-are-a-risk-to-food-security/.

26. "EU Agrees to World's Largest Green Fuels Mandate for Aviation", *Transport & Environment*, April 26, 2023, https://www.transportenvironment.org/discover/eu-agrees-to-worlds-largest-green-fuels-mandate-for-aviation/.

27. "Electrofuels for Aviation", *World Fund*, April 26, 2023, https://www.worldfund.vc/knowledge/electrofuels-for-aviation.

28. Prof. Haenel, Matthias W., "The Return of a Classic to Fuel Production", *Max Plank Gesellschaft*, December 14, 2005, https://www.mpg.de/511447/fischer-tropsch-synthesis-2005.

29. "Air Company: Breaking the Wall of Climate Change", *Falling Walls Foundation*, December 21, 2022, video, https://youtu.be/PI0hwUaO7g0.

30. Ibid.

31. Weber, Harri, "Startup Inks $65M Deal to Help Air Force Make 'Sustainable' Jet Fuel on Bases", *Tech Crunch*, February 28, 2023, https://techcrunch.com/2023/02/28/air-company-65m-deal-air-force-make-sustainable-jet-fuel-on-bases/.

32. Verger, Rob, "Why the US Military Plans to Start Making Its Own Jet Fuel", *Popular Science*, March 3, 2023, https://www.popsci.com/technology/us-military-synthetic-jet-fuel-air-company/.

33. Neimark, Benjamin, Belcher, Oliver, and Bigger, Patrick, "US Military Is a Bigger Polluter than as Many as 140 Countries – Shrinking This War Machine Is a Must", *The Conversation*, June 24, 2019, https://theconversation.com/us-military-is-a-bigger-polluter-than-as-many-as-140-countries-shrinking-this-war-machine-is-a-must-119269.

34. "U.S. Air Force Supported Start-Ups, Exosonic and Twelve Enter Partnership to Develop Supersonic Jet Compatible Sustainable Aviation Fuel", *Business Wire*, November 18, 2021, https://www.businesswire.com/news/home/20211118005981/en/U.S.-Air-Force-Supported-Start-Ups-Exosonic-and-Twelve-Enter-Partnership-to-Develop-Supersonic-Jet-Compatible-Sustainable-Aviation-Fuel.

35. "Air Company: Breaking the Wall of Climate Change", *Falling Walls Foundation*, December 21, 2022, video, https://youtu.be/PI0hwUaO7g0.

4. ARCHER AVIATION: BRINGING A FUTURISTIC VISION OF URBAN AIR MOBILITY TO THE MASSES TODAY WITH "REALISTIC INNOVATION"

1. Campbell, Rebecca, "eVTOL Companies Already Racking up Impressive Order Totals for Their Urban Aircraft", *Creamer Media's Engineering News*, September 12, 2022, https://www.engineeringnews.co.za/article/evtol-companies-already-racking-up-impressive-order-totals-for-their-urban-aircraft-2022-09-12.

2. "Hundreds of Space and Aviation Startups Are at Risk of Crumbling as VCs Warn Them to 'plan for the Worst'", *Business Insider*, September 12, 2022, https://www.businessinsider.com/hundreds-of-aerospace-startups-at-risk-of-crumbling-vc-funding-2022-7?r=US&IR=T.

3. Read more about Joby and Eve in Chapters 3 and 4, respectively.

4. "Flying Car Startup Archer May Be Poised to Soar Past Rivals like Joby in a $1 Trillion Market, JP Morgan Says. Here's why Analysts Call It an 'early Boarding Opportunity for Investors", *Business Insider*, May 10, 2022, https://www.businessinsider.com/archer-jp-morgan-joby-aviation-investors-evtol-flying-car-2022-5.

5. "Archer Open House | Commercialization Presentation", *Archer*, December 13, 2022, video, https://youtu.be/9989XjHJjV8?t=165.

6. Bogaisky, Jeremy, "With Money From Walmart'S Marc Lore, Stealth Startup Archer Buys Its Way Into The Electric Air Taxi Race", *Forbes*, May 21, 2020, https://www.forbes.com/sites/jeremybogaisky/2020/05/21/archer-walmart-marc-lore-electric-air-taxi/?sh=2aff56b1510e.

7. Nassauer, Sarah, "Wal-Mart to Acquire Jet.Com for $3.3 Billion in Cash, Stock", *The Wall Street Journal*, August 8, 2016, https://www.wsj.com/articles/wal-mart-to-acquire-jet-com-for-3-3-billion-in-cash-stock-1470659763.

8. Bogaisky, Jeremy, "With Money From Walmart'S Marc Lore, Stealth Startup Archer Buys Its Way Into The Electric Air Taxi Race", *Forbes*, May 21, 2020, https://www.forbes.com/sites/jeremybogaisky/2020/05/21/archer-walmart-marc-lore-electric-air-taxi/?sh=2aff56b1510e.

9. Nassauer, Sarah, "Flying Cars, Almost a Reality—Then the Lawyers Got Involved", *Fast Company*, August 7, 2022, https://www.fastcompany.com/90770701/flying-cars-almost-reality-wisk-boeing-archer-lawsuit.

10. "Archer", *Crunch Base*, August 7, 2022, https://www.crunchbase.com/organization/archer-b2aa/company_financials.

11. Patterson, Thom, "SPAC Shareholders Approve Merger With EVTOL Maker Archer Aviation", *Flying Mag*, September 14, 2021, https://www.flyingmag.com/archer-merger-approved/.

12. "United to Work with Archer Aviation to Accelerate Production of Advanced, Short-Haul Electric Aircraft", *PR Newswire*, February 10, 2021, https://www.prnewswire.com/news-releases/united-to-work-with-archer-aviation-to-accelerate-production-of-advanced-short-haul-electric-aircraft-301225798.html.

13. "Archer Taps FCA'S Scale and Expertise to Accelerate Electric Vertical Take Off and Landing Aircraft (EVTOL) Production", *Stellantis*, January 12,

2021,/https://media.stellantisnorthamerica.com/newsrelease.do?id=
22448&mid=1.

14. "Archer Investor Deck, 2021", Archer, https://s27.q4cdn.com/936913558/
    files/doc_presentations/Investor-Presentation.pdf.

15. "Take Off in a Flying Car With UF Engineers and Alumni", Herbert
    Wertheim College of Engineering - University of Florida, November 4, 2021,
    https://www.eng.ufl.edu/newengineer/alumni-spotlight/take-off-in-a-
    flying-car-with-uf-engineers-and-alumni/.

16. "Archer Lab Dedication Ceremony at the University of Florida", Archer,
    November 26, 2021, video, https://www.youtube.com/watch?v=3NHand
    LUifI.

17. "Vahana Has Come to an End. But a New Chapter at Airbus Has just Begun",
    Airbus, December 19, 2019, https://www.airbus.com/en/newsroom/
    stories/2019-12-vahana-has-come-to-an-end-but-a-new-chapter-at-airbus-
    has-just-begun.

18. Beckman, Brittany L., "Archer Reveals Its Maker Flying Taxi, Promising to
    Lift Us Out of Traffic Hell", *Mashable*, December 19, 2019, https://mashable.
    com/article/archer-maker-evtol-reveal.

19. Blain, Loz, "Archer's First Midnight EVTOL Is Built and Ready to Fly," *New
    Atlas*, May 11, 2023, https://newatlas.com/aircraft/archer-midnight-testing.

20. "Chicago Traffic Congestion Cost Commuters 104 Hours in 2021, Inrix Study
    Finds", *ABC 7 Chicago*, December 8, 2021, https://abc7chicago.com/traffic-
    chicago-i-55-report-map/11311515/.

21. "Archer And United Airlines Announce First Commercial Electric Air Taxi
    Route In The US: Downtown Manhattan To Newark Liberty International
    Airport", *Archer*, November 10, 2022, https://www.archer.com/news/
    archer-and-united-airlines-announce-first-commercial-electric-air-taxi-route-
    in-the-us-downtown-manhattan-to-newark-liberty-international-airport.

22. "United Airlines and Archer Announce First Commercial Electric Air Taxi
    Route in Chicago", *Archer*, March 23, 2023, https://investors.archer.com/
    news/news-details/2023/United-Airlines-and-Archer-Announce-First-
    Commercial-Electric-Air-Taxi-Route-in-Chicago/default.aspx.

23. "United Airlines and Archer Announce First Commercial Electric Air Taxi
    Route in Chicago", *Archer*, November 17, 2022, https://www.archer.com/
    news/archer-unveils-its-production-aircraft-midnight.

24. "Archer And REEF Team Up To Tackle Urban Congestion With Vertiports
    And Urban Air Mobility Networks", *Archer*, August 24, 2021, https://archer.
    com/news/archer-and-reef-team-up-to-tackle-urban-congestion-with-verti
    ports-and-urban-air-mobility-networks.

25. "Democratizing The Skies: EVTOL Cost And Accessibility", *Archer*, August
    27, 2021, https://archer.com/news/democratizing-the-skies-evtol-cost-and-
    accessibility.

26. Brinkmann, Paul. "Electric Air Taxi Flights in Los Angeles during the 2028
    Summer Olympics?", *Aerospace America*, April 13, 2023, https://aerospaceam
    erica.aiaa.org/electric-air-taxi-flights-in-los-angeles-during-the-2028-
    summer-olympics/.

27. "Archer Enters Agreement With United States Air Force To Collaborate On
    Flight Testing", *Archer*, September 3, 2021, https://archer.com/news/archer-

enters-agreement-with-united-states-air-force-to-collaborate-on-flight-testing.

28. "U.S. Air Force and Archer Enter Into Contracts Worth Up to $142 Million Representing Landmark Investment In EVTOL Technology by U.S. Military", *Business Wire*, September 3, 2021, https://www.businesswire.com/news/home/20230731089461/en/U.S.-Air-Force-and-Archer-Enter-Into-Contracts-Worth-Up-to-142-Million-Representing-Landmark-Investment-In-eVTOL-Technology-by-U.S.-Military.

29. Georgilidakis, Spyros, "Archer Aviation To Provide Six eVTOLs To US Air Force", *Mentour Pilot*, August 1, 2023, https://mentourpilot.com/archer-avia tion-to-provide-six-evtols-to-us-air-force/.

30. McNeil, Harry, "US Marine Corps Embraces Archer'S Midnight EVTOL Aircraft", *Airforce Technology*, August 3, 2023, https://www.airforce-technol ogy.com/news/us-marine-corps-embraces-archers-midnight-evtol-aircraft/.

31. "Archer EVTOL Deal with Air Force Could Ground Choppers", *Military Aerospace Electronics*, July 31, 2023, https://www.militaryaerospace.com/uncrewed/article/14297117/archer-evtol-deal-with-air-force-could-ground-choppers.

32. "Archer Aviation Forms Government Services Advisory Board to Support Planned Expansion of Its Existing Relationship With the U.S. Department of Defense", *Archer*, May 10, 2023, https://investors.archer.com/news/news-details/2023/Archer-Aviation-Forms-Government-Services-Advisory-Board-to-Support-Planned-Expansion-of-its-Existing-Relationship-With-the-U.S.-Department-of-Defense/default.aspx.

33. Kolodny, Lora, "Apple Loses Key Autos Engineer to Electric Aviation Startup Archer", *CNBC*, December 1, 2021, https://www.cnbc.com/2021/12/01/apple-ex-tesla-engineer-michael-schwekutsch-jumps-to-archer-avia tion.html.

34. https://www.molicel.com.

35. "Stellantis and Archer Team up to Manufacture Electric Aircraft", *CNBC Tele-vision*, January 4, 2023, video, https://www.youtube.com/watch?v=ptm9a0ud9dw&feature=youtu.be.

36. "Stellantis to Build Electric Aircraft with Archer and Provide Strategic Funding for Growth", *Stellantis*, January 4, 2023, https://www.stellantis.com/en/news/press-releases/2023/january/stellantis-to-build-electric-aircraft-with-archer-and-provide-strategic-funding-for-growth.

37. "Archer Closes Incentive Transaction; Begins Construction on First of Its Kind High-Volume eVTOL Manufacturing Facility in Covington, GA", *Archer*, March 7, 2023, https://investors.archer.com/news/news-details/2023/Archer-Closes-Incentive-Transaction-Begins-Construction-on-First-of-its-Kind-High-Volume-eVTOL-Manufacturing-Facility-in-Covington-GA/default.aspx.

38. "Billy Nolen, Former FAA Administrator, Joins Archer as Its Chief Safety Officer", *Archer*, June 13, 2023, https://investors.archer.com/news/news-details/2023/Billy-Nolen-Former-FAA-Administrator-Joins-Archer-as-Its-Chief-Safety-Officer/default.aspx.

39. Sampson, Ben, "Wisk Files Lawsuit against Competitor EVTOL Developer Archer", Aerospace Testing International, April 8, 2021, https://www.aero

spacetestinginternational.com/news/drones-air-taxis/wisk-files-lawsuit-against-competitor-evtol-developer-archer.html.

40. Rubin, Courtney, "Flying Cars, Almost a Reality—Then the Lawyers Got Involved", *Fast Company*, August 7, 2022, https://www.fastcompany.com/90770701/flying-cars-almost-reality-wisk-boeing-archer-lawsuit.

41. Alamalhodaei, Aria, "Electric Aircraft Makers Wisk and Archer End Bitter Legal Dispute, Agree to Work Together", *Tech Crunch*, August 10, 2023, https://techcrunch.com/2023/08/10/ending-bitter-court-battle-wisk-and-archer-collaborate/.

5. EMBRAER'S ROAD TO NET ZERO: "THE MISSION DEFINES THE ARCHITECTURE"

1. Campbell, Rebecca, "eVTOL companies already racking up impressive order totals for their urban aircraft and Joby outline a seamless, sustainable eVTOL passenger experience," *Creamer Media's Engineering News*, September 12, 2022, https://www.engineeringnews.co.za/article/evtol-companies-already-racking-up-impressive-order-totals-for-their-urban-aircraft-2022-09-12.

2. For more about Archer Aviation and Joby Aviation, read Chapters 8 and 3, respectively.

3. "Embraer - The Shape of Things to Come, New Sustainable Aircraft Concepts Revealed", Embraer, December 5, 2022, https://www.embraer.com/global/en/news?slug=1207138-embraer-the-shape-of-things-to-come-new-sustainable-aircraft-concepts-revealed.

4. Eve Air Mobility, "Urban Air Mobility: What's Next?", SXSW, March 13, 2023, https://schedule.sxsw.com/2023/events/PP131734.

5. "United Invests Another $15 Million in Electric Flying Taxi Market with Eve", Eve, September 8, 2022, https://eveairmobility.com/united-invests-another-15-million-in-electric-flying-taxi-market-with-eve/.

6. "United Airlines and Eve Air Mobility Collaborating to Bring First Electric Commuter Flights to San Francisco", Eve, June 14, 2023, https://eveairmobility.com/united-airlines-and-eve-air-mobility-collaborating-to-bring-first-electric-commuter-flights-to-san-francisco/.

7. Kamisher, Eliyahu, "Bay Area Drivers Spend 97 Hours a Year in Traffic. Why Didn't Remote Work End Commute Nightmares?", *The Mercury News*, March 31, 2023, https://www.mercurynews.com/2023/03/31/bay-area-drivers-spend-97-hours-a-year-in-traffic-why-didnt-remote-work-end-commute-nightmares/.

8. Rae, Alaisdair, "Mapping the Polycentric Metropolis: Journeys to Work in the Bay Area", *Under the Raedar*, July 12, 2015, http://www.undertheraedar.com/2015/07/mapping-polycentric-metrpololis.html.

9. "Eve and Kenya Airways' Fahari Aviation Sign an Agreement to Scale Urban Air Mobility with an Order of up to 40 eVTOLs to Fly People and Cargo", *Eve*, June 21, 2022, https://eveairmobility.com/eve-and-kenya-airways-fahari-aviation-sign-an-agreement-to-scale-urban-air-mobility-with-an-order-of-up-to-40-evtols-to-fly-people-and-cargo/.

10. Singer, Dirk, "Eve's Ambitions Take Centre Stage in Paris", *Sustainability in the Air*, June 27, 2023, https://green.simpliflying.com/p/eves-ambitions-take-centre-stage.

11. "Embraer's Eve and Widerøe Zero Collaborate to Develop Innovative Air Mobility Solutions in Scandinavia", Eve, September 10, 2021, https://eveair mobility.com/embraers-eve-and-wideroe-zero-collaborate-to-develop-innov ative-air-mobility-solutions-in-scandinavia/.

12. "Eve and Widerøe Zero Extend Partnership, Aiming to Launch eVTOL Operations in Scandinavia with Up to 50 Aircraft", Eve, June 20, 2023, https://ir.eveairmobility.com/news-events/press-releases/detail/35/eve-and-widere-zero-extend-partnership-aiming-to-launch.

13. Gabbatiss, Josh, "Norway to Make All Short-haul Flights Electric by 2040", *Independent*, January 18, 2018, https://www.independent.co.uk/climate-change/news/norway-short-haul-flights-electric-deadline-no-fossil-fuels-climate-change-a8165526.html.

14. Ewing, Jack, "In Norway, the Electric Vehicle Future Has Already Arrived", *The New York Times*, May 8, 2023, https://www.nytimes.com/2023/05/08/business/energy-environment/norway-electric-vehicles.html.

15. "Future Aircraft Concepts", Embraer Commercial Aviation, May 8, 2023, https://embraercommercialaviationsustainability.com/concepts/.

16. Schwab, Amy; Thomas; Anna, Bennet, Jesse et al, "Electrification of Aircraft: Challenges, Barriers, and Potential Impacts", *National Renewable Energy Laboratory (NREL)*, October 1, 2021, https://www.nrel.gov/docs/fy22osti/80220.pdf.

17. Embraer, "We've made history, again!...", Facebook, July 1, 2022, https://www.facebook.com/Embraer/posts/1180271429461057/.

18. Embraer, "Embraer, Raízen Partnership to Stimulate Production of Sustainable Aviation Fuel", *Biobased Diesel Daily*, July 19, 2022, https://www.biobased-diesel.com/post/embraer-ra%C3%ADzen-partnership-to-stimu late-production-of-sustainable-aviation-fuel.

19. "Phenom 300E", *Embraer*, July 19, 2022, https://executive.embraer.com/global/en/phenom-300e.

6. JETBLUE'S AMBITIOUS PUSH TO DECARBONISE AVIATION

1. Boehm, Sophie and Schumer, Clea, "10 Big Findings from the 2023 IPCC Report on Climate Change", World Resources Institute, March 20, 2023, https://www.wri.org/insights/2023-ipcc-ar6-synthesis-report-climate-change-findings.

2. "Uber, JetBlue Join Amazon-backed Climate Pledge", *Reuters*, December 2, 2020, https://www.reuters.com/article/us-amazon-com-climatechange/uber-jetblue-join-amazon-backed-climate-pledge-idINKBN28C24H.

3. "Be the Planet's Turning Point," The Climate Pledge, 2023, https://www.theclimatepledge.com/.

4. Cardwell, Diane, "JetBlue Makes Biofuels Deal to Curtail Greenhouse Gases", *The New York Times*, September 19, 2016, https://www.nytimes.com/

2016/09/20/business/energy-environment/jetblue-makes-biofuels-deal-to-curtail-greenhouse-gases.html.

5. JetBlue and The Nature Conservancy, "New Report from JetBlue and The Nature Conservancy Uses AI Technology to Evaluate the Impact of Natural Resources on Tourism", *Business Wire*, January 15, 2019, https://www.businesswire.com/news/home/20190115005650/en/New-Report-from-JetBlue-and-The-Nature-Conservancy-Uses-AI-Technology-to-Evaluate-the-Impact-of-Natural-Resources-on-Tourism.

6. "Best CEO in the Sustainable Aviation Industry: Robin Hayes", European CEO Awards 2018, https://www.europeanceo.com/awards-2018/best-ceos/3.

7. "How JetBlue Balances Sustainability With Growth", *Bloomberg Television*, October 23, 2019, video, https://www.youtube.com/watch?v=AWc6Wx0o0Qw.

8. Unnikrishnan, Madhu, "JetBlue CEO Warns Flight Shaming Is Coming to the U.S.", *Skift*, January 23, 2020, https://skift.com/2020/01/23/jetblue-ceo-warns-flight-shaming-is-coming-to-the-u-s/.

9. O'Brien, Casey, "JetBlue Embarks on Journey to Offset All U.S. Domestic Flights", *GreenBiz*, January 14, 2020, https://www.greenbiz.com/article/jetblue-embarks-journey-offset-all-us-domestic-flights.

10. McGurty, Janet, "JetBlue Airways Stitches Sustainability into Its Growth Strategy", *S&P Global Commodity Insights*, July 27, 2021, https://www.spglobal.com/commodityinsights/en/market-insights/latest-news/agriculture/072721-jetblue-airways-stitches-sustainability-into-its-growth-strategy.

11. "Ambitious Corporate Climate Action", Science Based Targets (SBTi), https://sciencebasedtargets.org/.

12. "JetBlue Announces Science-based Emissions Reduction Target and Strategy to Achieve Net Zero by 2040", JetBlue, December 6, 2022, https://ir.jetblue.com/news/news-details/2022/JetBlue-Announces-Science-based-Emissions-Reduction-Target-and-Strategy-to-Achieve-Net-Zero-by-2040-12-06-2022/default.aspx.

13. Singer, Dirk, "JetBlue Releases Science Based Targets", *Sustainability in the Air*, December 8, 2022, https://green.simpliflying.com/p/jetblue-releases-net-zero-targets.

14. For more about JetBlue's sustainability efforts, see Chapter 3.

15. United, "United's Sustainable Flight Fund Grows to Nearly $200 Million and Adds Strategic Partners", *PR Newswire*, July 25, 2023, https://www.prnewswire.com/news-releases/uniteds-sustainable-flight-fund-grows-to-nearly-200-million-and-adds-strategic-partners-301884475.html.

16. Brandler, Hannah, "JetBlue Allows Passengers to Purchase SAF", Business Traveller, March 1, 2023, https://www.businesstraveller.com/business-travel/2023/03/01/jetblue-allows-passengers-to-purchase-saf/.

17. Surgenor, Christopher, "JetBlue Launches Corporate Sustainable Travel Programme with a Focus on Offering SAF Certificates", *Green Air News*, January 7, 2022, https://www.greenairnews.com/?p=2350.

18. Singer, Dirk, "FORMIA Showcases a Range of Sustainable Amenity Kit Products at APEX/IFSA EXPO", IFSA, October 26, 2022, https://apex.aero/articles/formia-apex-expo/.

19. Schlangenstein, Mary (with Bloomberg), "JetBlue Is Dumping American Airlines in a Last-ditch Attempt to Win Approval for Its Spirit Airlines Acquisition", *Fortune*, July 6, 2023, https://fortune.com/2023/07/06/jetblue-dumping-american-airlines-attempt-win-approval-spirit-airlines-acquisition/.

20. JetBlue Technology Ventures, "JetBlue Technology Ventures Invests in Universal Hydrogen to Support the Airline's Ambitious Sustainability Strategy", *Business Wire*, April 22, 2021, https://www.businesswire.com/news/home/20210422005923/en/JetBlue-Technology-Ventures-Invests-in-Universal-Hydrogen-to-Support-the-Airline%E2%80%99s-Ambitious-Sustainability-Strategy.

21. Avnos, "Avnos Inc. Secures Funding and Strategic Partnerships From ConocoPhillips, JetBlue Ventures and Shell Ventures, Totaling Over $80M", *Business Wire*, July 22, 2023. https://www.businesswire.com/news/home/20230713885165/en/Avnos-Inc.-Secures-Funding-and-Strategic-Partnerships-From-ConocoPhillips-JetBlue-Ventures-and-Shell-Ventures-Totaling-Over-80M.

22. "i6: A cloud-based digital fuel management platform", JetBlue Ventures, July 22, 2023, https://www.jetblueventures.com/portfolio/i6/.

23. Peters, Kelly, "Tomorrow.Io Selected to Provide Weather Forecasting Technology Throughout All of JetBlue's Flight Operations", Tomorrow, November 8, 2022, https://www.tomorrow.io/blog/tomorrow-io-selected-to-provide-weather-forecasting-technology-throughout-all-of-jetblues-flight-operations/.

24. For more on Air Company, see Chapter 6.

25. "More than One Quarter of All Venture Capital Funding Is Going to Climate Technology, with Increased Focus on Technologies that Have the Most Potential to Cut Emissions", *PwC*, March 11, 2022, https://www.pwc.com/gx/en/news-room/press-releases/2022/state-of-climate-tech-report-2022.html.

26. Russell, Molly, "JetBlue Reveals How It Intends To Get To Net-Zero By 2040", *Simple Flying*, December 6, 2022, https://simpleflying.com/jetblue-net-zero-by-2040-strategy.

27. Harris, Mark, "Universal Hydrogen Takes to the Air with the Largest Hydrogen Fuel Cell Ever to Fly", *Tech Crunch*, March 2, 2023, https://techcrunch.com/2023/03/02/universal-hydrogen-takes-to-the-air-with-the-largest-hydrogen-fuel-cell-ever-to-fly/.

28. Read more about ZeroAvia in Chapter 7.

29. Madler, Mark R., "Universal Hydrogen Reaches Milestone", *Los Angeles Business Journal*, March 20, 2023, https://labusinessjournal.com/transportation/aviation/universal-hydrogen-reaches-milestone/.

30. Universal Hydrogen, "Universal Hydrogen and Connect Airlines Announce Firm Order for Conversion of 75 ATR 72-600 Regional Aircraft to Be Powered by Green Hydrogen", *Business Wire*, June 9, 2022, https://www.businesswire.com/news/home/20220608006035/en/Universal-Hydrogen-and-Connect-Airlines-Announce-Firm-Order-for-Conversion-of-75-ATR-72-600-Regional-Aircraft-to-Be-Powered-by-Green-Hydrogen.

31. EP Systems, "Electric Battery Aviation Leader Electric Power Systems Announces Strategic Partnership with Regent Craft," *Business Wire*, April 20, 2023, https://www.businesswire.com/news/home/20230420005601/en/Electric-Battery-Aviation-Leader-Electric-Power-Systems-Announces-Strategic-Partnership-with-Regent-Craft.

32. "Electric Battery Aviation Leader Electric Power Systems Announces Strategic Partnership with Regent Craft", *The Engineer*, July 25, 2022, https://www.theengineer.co.uk/content/news/hybrid-electric-eel-aircraft-sets-distance-record.

33. "Joby Reports $1.1 Billion in Hand at Close of Fourth Quarter", *Flying Media*, February 23, 2023, https://www.flyingmag.com/joby-reports-1-1-billion-in-hand-at-close-of-fourth-quarter/.

34. Joby Aviation, "Joby Aviation Secures $100M in Series B Funding to Make Electric Vertical Take-off and Landing Transportation a Reality", *Business Wire*, February 1, 2018, https://www.businesswire.com/news/home/20180201005422/en/Joby-Aviation-Secures-100M-in-Series-B-Funding-to-Make-Electric-Vertical-Take-off-and-Landing-Transportation-a-Reality.

35. "Joby Begins Testing at the World's Largest Wind Tunnel Facility", Joby Aviation, February 16, 2023, https://www.jobyaviation.com/news/joby-begins-testing-at-worlds-largest-wind-tunnel-nasa/.

36. Shephardson, David, "Delta Air Invests $60 Mln, Takes Stake in Air Taxi Startup Joby Aviation", *Reuters* October 11, 2022, https://www.reuters.com/business/aerospace-defense/delta-air-invests-60-mln-takes-stake-air-taxi-startup-joby-aviation-2022-10-11/.

37. Singer, Dirk, "Delta Airlines and Joby Outline a Seamless, Sustainable EVTOL Passenger Experience", *Apex*, March 18, 2023, https://apex.aero/articles/delta-joby/.

7. ETIHAD'S FOCUS ON NET-ZERO EMISSIONS TODAY

1. Pilling, Mark, "The green dream", *Times Aerospace*, June 23, 2022, https://www.timesaerospace.aero/features/sustainability/the-green-dream.

2. "COP28 Host UAE Pledges to Triple Renewables," *France 24*, March 7, 2023, https://www.france24.com/en/live-news/20230703-cop28-host-uae-pledges-to-triple-renewables.

3. "Etihad Greenliner Programme", *Etihad Aviation Group*, March 7, 2023, https://www.etihadaviationgroup.com/en-ae/about/sustainability/green liner.

4. Ahlgren, Linnea, "What Is The Etihad Airways Greenliner Program?", *Simple Flying*, October 20, 2021, https://simpleflying.com/eithad-airways-green liner-program/.

5. Prisco, Jacopo, "Etihad's 'Greenliner' Shows a Glimpse of a More Sustainable Future for Aviation", *CNN* December 9, 2022, https://edition.cnn.com/travel/article/ethiad-greenliner-sustainable-aviation-climate-spc-intl/index.html.

6. "The Future of Net Zero Aviation", Office of the UAE Special Envoy for Climate Change, November 16, 2022, video, https://www.youtube.-

com/live/caNr9wRLTcY.

7. Ibid., 122.

8. "Etihad Airways Flies the World's First Flight on Salicornia Derived Fuel from the UAE", *Bioenergy International*, January 17, 2019, https://bioenergyin ternational.com/etihad-airways-flies-the-worlds-first-flight-on-salicornia-derived-fuel-from-the-uae/.

9. "Sustainable Bioenergy Research Consortium (SBRC)", International Civil Aviation Organization (ICAO), https://www.icao.int/environmental-protec tion/GFAAF/Pages/Project.aspx?ProjectID=21.

10. Grieve, Chuck, "Planting the Seed of Our Sustainable Future", *Times Aerospace*, June 14, 2023, https://www.timesaerospace.aero/features/sustainabil ity/planting-the-seed-of-our-sustainable-future.

11. Read more about the production of green hydrogen in Chapter 7.

12. Martin, Polly and Parkes, Rachel, "UAE Targets 15 Million Tonnes of Green Hydrogen Production by 2050 as It Approves National H2 Strategy", July 4, 2023, https://www.hydrogeninsight.com/policy/uae-targets-15-million-tonnes-of-green-hydrogen-production-by-2050-as-it-approves-national-h2-strategy/2-1-1480383.

13. Read more about companies pioneering hydrogen power in Chapters 7 and 3 on ZeroAvia and JetBlue Ventures, respectively.

14. Twelve, "Twelve and Etihad Airways Partner to Advance Sustainable Aviation Fuel Made from CO2 and Renewable Energy", *Business Wire*, May 11, 2023, https://www.businesswire.com/news/home/20230511005131/en/Twelve-and-Etihad-Airways-partner-to-advance-sustainable-aviation-fuel-made-from-CO2-and-renewable-energy.

15. "Non-CO2 Effects of Aviation", *Transport & Environment*, https://www.trans portenvironment.org/challenges/planes/airplane-pollution/non-co2-effects/.

16. Lee, D.S., Fahey, D.W., Skowron, A. et al, "The Contribution of Global Aviation to Anthropogenic Climate Forcing for 2000 to 2018", *Atmospheric Environment 244*, November 11, 2020, https://www.sciencedirect.com/science/article/pii/S1352231020305689.

17. Prisco, Jacopo, "Contrails Are a Problem for Aviation – but There Could Be an Easy Solution", *CNN Travel*, January 12, 2023, https://edition.cnn.com/travel/article/contrails-aviation-climate-change-satavia-scn-spc-intl/index.html.

18. "The Future of Net Zero Aviation", Office of the UAE Special Envoy for Climate Change, November 16, 2022, video, https://www.youtube.com/live/caNr9wRLTcY.

19. "Etihad Mangrove Forest," Etihad, https://www.etihad.com/en/sustainabil ity/how-to-get-involved/etihad-mangrove-forest.

20. "Mangroves for coastal defence: Guidelines for coastal managers & policy makers", *Wetlands International and the Nature Conservancy*, 2014, https://www.nature.org/media/oceansandcoasts/mangroves-for-coastal-defence.pdf.

21. "Etihad Airways Named Environmental Airline of the Year 2023", Etihad, May 31, 2023, https://www.etihad.com/en-gb/news/etihad-airways-named-environmental-airline-of-the-year-2023.

8. SKYTEAM'S SUSTAINABLE FLIGHT CHALLENGE: BRIDGING HISTORY AND INNOVATION IN AIR TRAVEL

1. "How UK-Australia Journey Went from 28 Days to 17 Hours in 100 Years," *Independent*, March 22, 2018, https://www.independent.co.uk/travel/news-and-advice/uk-australia-flight-time-travel-100-years-change-london-perth-direct-a8268311.html.
2. "Inflation Calculator," Bank of England, https://www.bankofengland.co.uk/monetary-policy/inflation/inflation-calculator.
3. "MacRobertson Air Race," *Wikipedia*, https://en.wikipedia.org/wiki/MacRobertson_Air_Race.
4. "1934 London to Melbourne Air Race – The Flight of KLM Uiver," *Spice Islands Blog*, April 27, 2020, https://spiceislandsblog.com/2020/04/27/1934-london-to-melbourne-air-race-the-flight-of-klm-uiver/.
5. "Our Members," SkyTeam, https://www.skyteam.com/en/about/our-members/
6. The Sustainable Flight Challenge 2022 - https://sustainableflightchallenge.com/default/content/TSFG2022Page
7. "SkyTeam's Sustainable Flight Challenge 2023 Takes Off, Charting Path to Cleaner Skies," *SkyTeam*, https://www.skyteam.com/en/about/press-releases/press-releases-2023/sustainable-flight-challenge-2023-takes-off/.
8. "KQ to Pilot Use of Sustainable Aviation Fuel During the Sustainable Flight Challenge," Kenya Airways, May 11, 2022, https://corporate.kenya-airways.com/en/news-press-release/2023/may/kq-to-pilot-use-of-sustainable-avia tion-fuel-during-the-sustainable-flight-challenge/.
9. "China Airlines Sustainability Flight Leads the Way with Low Carbon Meals and Net Zero Carbon Emissions," China Airlines, May 22, 2023, https://www.china-airlines.com/sea/id/discover/news/press-release/20230522.
10. Nigam, Shashank, "How Saudia Is Delivering on Brand EXpression in the Age of Sustainability," *Sustainability in the Air*, May 22, 2023, https://green.simpliflying.com/p/how-saudia-is-delivering-on-brand-expression-in-the-age-of-sustainability.
11. "Fly Sustainably," SAUDIA, https://www.saudia.com/Pages/experience/explore/sustainability?sc_lang=en&sc_country=US.
12. "Viasat Helps Aeromexico Perform Its Most Sustainable Flight Yet," *Viasat*, May 11, 2022, https://news.viasat.com/blog/gem/viasat-helps-aeromexico-perform-its-most-sustainable-flight-yet.
13. "Delta Introduces Artisan-made Amenity Kits from Mexican Apparel Brand Someone Somewhere," Delta, January 25, 2022, https://news.delta.com/delta-introduces-artisan-made-amenity-kits-mexican-apparel-brand-some one-somewhere.
14. "Delta Participates in SkyTeam'S Sustainable Flight Challenge, Showcases Sustainability Strategy in Action," Delta, May 24, 2023, https://news.delta.com/delta-participates-skyteams-sustainable-flight-challenge-showcases-sustainability-strategy-action.
15. "Vietnam Airlines Performs Sustainable Flight to Frankfurt," *Business Traveller*, June 1, 2023, https://www.businesstraveller.com/business-travel/

2023/06/01/vietnam-airlines-performs-sustainable-flight-to-frankfurt/.

16. "Air France Halves CO2 Emissions on Two of Its Flights with a Series of Actions to Limit Its Environmental Footprint," Air France, https://corpo rate.airfrance.com/en/news/air-france-halves-co2-emissions-two-its-flights-series-actions-limit-its-environmental.

17. Tandon, Ayesha, "'Food Miles' Have Larger Climate Impact than Thought, Study Suggests," *Carbon Brief*, June 20, 2022, https://www.carbonbrief.org/food-miles-have-larger-climate-impact-than-thought-study-suggests/.

18. "China Airlines Sustainability Flight Leads the Way with Low Carbon Meals and Net Zero Carbon Emissions," China Airlines, May 22, 2023, https://www.china-airlines.com/sea/id/discover/news/press-release/20230522.

19. "Kenya Airways In-flight Catering Scores High in SkyTeam Sustainability Challenge," *256 Business News*, July 15, 2022, https://www.256businessnews.com/kenya-airways-in-flight-catering-scores-high-in-skyteam-challenge/.

20. Bailey, Joanna, "Airlines Burn $4 Billion Of Untouched Food And Drink Every Year – Here's Why," *Simple Flying*, December 7, 2022, https://simple flying.com/airlines-4-billion-untouched-food-drink/.

21. Saunders, Eddie, "Vietnam Airlines Completes SkyTeam 'Sustainable Flight Challenge'," ARGS, June 9, 2023, https://airlinergs.com/vietnam-airlines-completes-skyteam-sustainable-flight-challenge/.

22. Rowland, Becca, "Which Part of a Flight Uses the Most Fuel?", OAG, February 3, 2022, https://www.oag.com/blog/which-part-flight-uses-most-fuel.

23. Measured in RTK and compared to a set of baseline flights from the month prior to the TSFC flights

AVIATION IS IN THE LAST CHANCE SALOON—HERE'S WHAT WE NEED TO DO NOW

1. https://www.linkedin.com/in/brita-staal/.

2. France-Presse, Agence, "Greece Faces Hottest July Weekend in 50 Years, Forecaster Says, as Scores of Wildfires Rage", *The Guardian*, July 21, 2023, https://www.theguardian.com/world/2023/jul/22/greece-faces-hottest-july-weekend-in-50-years-forecaster-says-as-scores-of-wildfires-rage.

3. Halliday, Josh, "British Tourists Tell of 'Living Nightmare' as 19,000 Evacuated in Rhodes Fires", *The Guardian*, July 23, 2023, https://www.the-guardian.com/world/2023/jul/23/british-tourists-tell-of-nightmare-in-rhodes-fires-greece.

4. Lockyer, Chris, and Robinson, James. "Rhodes Wildfires: British Tourist Says Trying to Escape the Flames 'was Literally like the End of the World'", *Sky News*, July 23, 2023, https://news.sky.com/story/rhodes-wildfires-british-tourist-says-trying-to-escape-the-flames-was-literally-like-the-end-of-the-world-12925804.

5. Staal, Brita, "Thoughts from a Scalding Athens in a Climate in Crisis", *We Don't Have Time*, July, 2023, https://app.wedonthavetime.org/posts/5b5f-f6d0-31ae-4a40-88aa-fccac8a20938.

6. Ibid.

7. Mishra, Stuti, "China Shatters All-time High Temperature Record with a Sizzling 52.2C", *Independent*, July 17, 2023, https://www.independent.co.uk/climate-change/news/china-heatwave-2023-record-temperature-b2376587.html.

8. Oladipo, Gloria; Rawlinson, Kevin; Gayle, Damien et al, "Extreme Weather Live: Phoenix Breaks Record with 19th Day of 110F Highs in a Row; Europe Swelters under Heatwave – as It Happened", *The Guardian*, July 18, 2023, https://www.theguardian.com/environment/live/2023/jul/18/europe-heat-wave-2023-us-asia-heatwave-live-updates-extreme-severe-weather-hottest-record-temperature-red-alert-climate-crisis-latest-news.

9. Mann, Charles C., 2018, *The Wizard and the Prophet: Two Views of the Future*, Penguin Random House.

10. Lamb, William F.; Mattoli, Giulio; and Levi, Sebastian, "Discourses of Climate Delay", *Global Sustainability 3*, (2020),. https://www.cambridge.org/core/journals/global-sustainability/article/discourses-of-climate-delay/7B11B722E3E3454BB6212378E32985A7.

11. https://www.un.org/sg/en/content/sg/statement/2022-02-28/secretary-generals-video-message-the-press-conference-launch-of-ipcc-report-scroll-down-for-languages

12. Sharma, Sukalp, "India Could Become Top Aviation Market Globally by Decade-end: Civil Aviation Secretary Bansal", Indian Express, March 21, 2023, https://indianexpress.com/article/business/aviation/india-could-become-top-aviation-market-globally-by-decade-end-civil-aviation-secretary-bansal-8509562/.

13. "National Green Hydrogen Mission: Decarbonising India, Achieving Net-Zero Vision", National Portal of India, March 21, 2023, https://www.india.gov.in/spotlight/national-green-hydrogen-mission.

14. Gayle, Damien, "Just One of 50 Aviation Industry Climate Targets Met, Study Finds", *The Guardian*, May 10, 2022, https://www.theguardian.com/environment/2022/may/10/just-one-of-50-aviation-industry-climate-targets-met-study-finds.

15. Clements, Poppy, "United's Sustainable Flight Fund Grows to Nearly US$200 Million", Hydrocarbon Engineering, July 26, 2023, https://www.hydrocarbonengineering.com/clean-fuels/26072023/uniteds-sustainable-flight-fund-grows-to-nearly-us200-million/.

16. Kommenda, Nigo, "How Your Flight Emits as Much CO2 as Many People Do in a Year", *The Guardian*, July 19, 2019, https://www.theguardian.com/environment/ng-interactive/2019/jul/19/carbon-calculator-how-taking-one-flight-emits-as-much-as-many-people-do-in-a-year/.

17. Rowland, Becca, "Which Part of a Flight Uses the Most Fuel?", *OAG*, February 3, 2022, https://www.oag.com/blog/which-part-flight-uses-most-fuel.

18. Badola, Ayushi, "How Scott Kirby Is Making United Airlines a Global Leader in Sustainability", *Sustainability in the Air*, May 4, 2022, https://green.simpliflying.com/p/scott-kirby-ceo-united-airlines#details.

19. "France Bans Short-haul Flights to Cut Carbon Emissions", *BBC*, May 23, 2023, https://www.bbc.co.uk/news/world-europe-65687665.

MORE INNOVATORS TO LOOK OUT FOR

1. "Ampaire Vehicles - Meet the Eco Caravan", Ampaire, July 26, 2023, https://www.ampaire.com/vehicles.

2. "Hybrid-electric EEL Aircraft Sets Distance Record", *The Engineer*, July 25, 2022, https://www.theengineer.co.uk/content/news/hybrid-electric-eel-aircraft-sets-distance-record.

3. Shanshan, Chen, "China's CATL, COMAC Are Poised to Start Developing Electric Planes, Insiders Say", *Yicai Global*, July 21, 2023, https://www.yicaiglobal.com/news/chinas-catl-comac-are-poised-to-start-developing-electric-planes-insiders-say.

4. "Aviation", International Trade Administration, July 4, 2023, https://www.trade.gov/country-commercial-guides/china-aviation.

5. Zandt, Florian, "China Leads the Way in Electrifying the Road", *Statista*, July 21, 2023, https://www.statista.com/chart/30452/countries-with-the-most-bev-sales-per-year/.

6. Frayer, Janis M., and Gao, Larissa, "Chinese Electric Vehicle Makers Lead the World, Rivaling U.S. Pioneers", *NBC News*, July 18, 2023, https://www.nbcnews.com/news/world/chinese-electric-vehicle-makers-lead-world-rivaling-us-pioneers-rcna88990.

7. "Britten-Norman to Merge with Cranfield Hydrogen Fuel Cell Firm", *Flyer*, April 24, 2023, https://flyer.co.uk/britten-norman-to-merge-with-cranfield-hydrogen-fuel-cell-firm/.

8. "Cranfield Eyes $37m Funding to Develop Hydrogen-powered Aircraft", *Verdict*, June 5, 2023, https://www.verdict.co.uk/cranfield-hydrogen-powered-aircraft/.

9. Kamczyc, Alex, "Fulcrum BioEnergy Successfully Produces Low-carbon Fuel from Landfill Waste", *Waste Today*, December 20, 2022, https://www.wastetodaymagazine.com/news/fulcrum-bioenergy-produces-low-carbon-fuel-from-landfill-waste/.

10. "Fulcrum BioEnergy's United Kingdom Waste-To-Fuels Project Awarded £16.8 Million Grant from the UK Department for Transport Advanced Fuels Fund", *PR Newswire*, February 16, 2023, https://www.prnewswire.com/news-releases/fulcrum-bioenergys-united-kingdom-waste-to-fuels-project-awarded-16-8-million-grant-from-the-uk-department-for-transport-advanced-fuels-fund-301748337.html.

11. Wichter, Zach, "A Garbage Team: United Airlines and Sesame Street Partner on Green Education Campaign", *USA Today*, March 6, 2023, https://eu.usatoday.com/story/travel/airline-news/2023/03/02/united-airlines-oscar-the-grouch-sustainable-fuel/11376777002/.

12. Singer, Dirk, "From Retro Inspiration To Futuristic Mobility: LYTE Aviation's SkyBus", *Sustainability in the Air*, July 18, 2023, https://green.simpliflying.com/p/from-retro-inspiration-to-futuristic.

13. Singer, Dirk. "Maeve Looks to Build a New Family of Net Zero Regional Aircraft." *Sustainability in the Air.* May 30, 2023. https://green.simpliflying.com/p/maeve-looks-to-build-a-new-family.

14. Singer, Dirk, "Magpie Aims to Build an 'Electric Tow Network for the Skies'", *Sustainability in the Air*, May 16, 2023, https://green.simpliflying.-

com/p/magpie-aims-to-build-an-electric.

15. "Twelve" Twelve, May 16, 2023, https://www.twelve.co/.

16. "Twelve Commences Construction of First Commercial-Scale Plant in US for Producing Sustainable Aviation Fuel from CO2", *PR Newswire*, July 11, 2023, https://www.businesswire.com/news/home/20230711105932/en/Twelve-Commences-Construction-of-First-Commercial-Scale-Plant-in-US-for-Producing-Sustainable-Aviation-Fuel-from-CO2.

17. "Wisk", Wisk, https://wisk.aero.

18. Bodell, Luke, "Wisk Aero Is Now A Fully-Owned Boeing Subsidiary", *Simple Flying*, June 8, 2023, https://simpleflying.com/wisk-aero-boeing-subsidiary/.

19. Hardee, Howard, "Potential eVTOL Showcase at 2028 Summer Olympics 'Very Interesting': Wisk", *Flight Global*, June 19, 2023, https://www.flightglobal.com/air-transport/potential-evtol-showcase-at-2028-summer-olympics-very-interesting-wisk/153769.article.

MORE INNOVATORS TO LOOK OUT FOR

The innovators we have profiled in this book are only a small selection of all the different organisations looking to decarbonise aviation.

As a result, here are 10 more that we think hold promise and are worth your time looking into. We may well include some in future editions of this book.

AMPAIRE

California based Ampaire is focused on integrating hybrid electric propulsion technology into existing aircraft, starting with the Cessna Grand Caravan, the retrofitted version of which will be called the Eco Caravan.[1] Ampaire hopes to have the aircraft certified as soon as 2024.

Ampaire believes that its retrofitting approach to small regional aircraft offers a cost-effective and practical solution for achieving efficiency and reducing carbon emissions, and one that can be done now.

At time of writing, Ampaire holds the record for the longest hybrid electric non-stop flight (from California to Kansas).[2]

CATL/COMAC

In the Introduction, we talked about China's CATL developing a 500 wh/kg battery that has the potential to revolutionise electric flight. CATL has now joined forces with Chinese aircraft manufacturer COMAC and Shanghai Jiao Tong University in a joint venture that will make electric aircraft.[3]

This is significant, not only because China is the world's second largest civil aerospace market.[4] The country has also become the leader when it comes to sales of electric cars,[5] including developing a large electric vehicle manufacturing industry.[6]

As a result, with China already having a strong track record in electrifying transport, this new joint venture could end up being quite groundbreaking.

CRANFIELD AEROSPACE SOLUTIONS

A spin-off from Cranfield University, which among other things specialises in postgraduate aviation research, Cranfield Aerospace Solutions is developing hydrogen-powered planes. In 2023, the company merged with Britten-Norman, the manufacturer of the Islander aircraft.[7]

Though the new company is starting small by retrofitting a nine seat Britten-Norman Islander with hydrogen-electric technology, the ultimate aim is to produce a regional jet capable of carrying 100 passengers.[8]

Cranfield's pedigree and the Britten-Norman merger makes this one to watch.

FULCRUM BIOENERGY

Fulcrum BioEnergy turns landfill waste into SAF. Their process turns municipal trash into synthetic crude oil, which can then be further refined into jet fuel and other fuels.

Fulcrum has a plant in Reno, Nevada that is the world's first commercial-scale landfill waste to low-carbon transportation fuels plant.[9] The company is also planning on opening up a facility in the United Kingdom.[10]

The company has already secured major investors like United Airlines, who mentioned Fulcrum in its own marketing efforts in 2023 using the Sesame Street character Oscar the Grouch to explain how trash might be turned into SAF.[11]

LYTE AVIATION

UK and Germany-based LYTE Aviation is developing a 44-seat hybrid hydrogen-electric eVTOL called the LA-44 SkyBus, aiming to revolutionise air transportation by carrying a significantly larger number of passengers than traditional eVTOLs (electric vertical takeoff and landing aircraft).[12]

LYTE believes its SkyBus can serve a wide range of use cases due to its capacity, 1000 km range, and the fact that it only needs a vertiport to fly rather than a runway. Once scaled, LYTE's aircraft could potentially eliminate the need for train tracks and highways in remote areas, in turn helping to preserve the local environment.

MAEVE AEROSPACE

Dutch electric aircraft manufacturer Maeve Aerospace expects its first aircraft, the all-electric Maeve 01, to be in service by the end of the decade. This will be a fully electric regional aircraft able to carry 44 passengers and a range of 250 nautical miles (460 km), excluding reserves.[13]

Because Maeve believes that only 40+ passenger aircraft will be attractive to operators, it is concentrating on building larger planes to compete directly with the workhorses of regional aviation, such as the ATR family of turboprops.

MAGPIE

Magpie has a very novel solution to electric flight by developing towing aircraft with space for electric batteries, a pilot, and little else.[14] These aircraft will tow other passenger-carrying electric aircraft or conventionally-powered planes through the skies in a series of relays.

Magpie aims for its solution to be cost-effective—namely, cheaper than a SAF-powered journey would be on the same route—because its tow planes will take off and land from secondary airports. Of course, unlike SAF, these journeys will be true-zero and completely emissions-free.

TWELVE

Similar to Air Company, Twelve is a carbon transformation company that makes products directly from the air.[15] Twelve has been looking at products such as fossil-free plastics, sustainable clothing made from CO_2, and jet fuel—and in July 2023, Twelve broke ground on what will be its first commercial e-fuel facility, in Washington State.[16]

With a 2040 net-zero target like JetBlue, Alaska Airlines is already an investor and partner of Twelve. Other major partnerships include Twelve's agreement to produce e-fuels for Etihad, as we detailed in Chapter 2.

WISK

As an eVTOL maker, Wisk is skipping the development of piloted aircraft and going directly to autonomous flight.[17] That means its eVTOLs will fly without a pilot, but will be controlled by operators on the ground.

Wisk currently benefits from being a subsidiary of aircraft giant Boeing, just as Eve benefits from the support of its parent company Embraer (as discussed earlier in this book).[18] Though

Wisk has not set a certification date, it is eyeing the LA Olympics in 2028 as a time to showcase its technology.[19]

WANT TO KNOW MORE? LISTEN TO OUR PODCAST AND READ THE INSIGHTS ON OUR WEBSITE

Hosted by SimpliFlying CEO and Founder Shashank Nigam, *Sustainability in the Air* was the world's first sustainable aviation podcast.

Over the past year, aviation CEO guests have included Scott Kirby (United Airlines), Tony Douglas (formerly Etihad, now Riyadh Air), Patrick Roux (SkyTeam), Paul Griffiths (Dubai Airports), and John Pagano (Red Sea Global).

The show has additionally featured all of the innovators in this book such as Heart Aerospace's Anders Forslund, Archer Aviation's Adam Goldstein, and ZeroAvia's Val Miftakhov.

You can listen to all the shows here:
https://simpliflying.com/podcast/

Meanwhile, our *Sustainability in the Air* website includes weekly articles on sustainable aviation tech startups, reports on subjects as diverse as SAF and eVTOLs, and regular newsletters telling thousands of industry subscribers the information that they need about aviation's mission to overcome the problems of climate change.

Subscribe today to stay ahead of the competition:
https://green.simpliflying.com/

ACKNOWLEDGEMENTS

Completing *Sustainability in the Air* has been a journey of collaboration and tireless dedication. We are profoundly grateful to the individuals and organisations who made this endeavour possible.

Our quest for a publisher took us down a long road, where we encountered hurdles like huge upfront costs and publication timelines of as long as a year. That was until Shashank found Legacy Launch Pad Publishing in Los Angeles. In a world where the aviation industry's news cycle moves fast, they were able to transform our manuscript into printed books within a matter of weeks.

At the heart of our project was our editor, Ryan Aliapoulios. Crafting a book about sustainable aviation requires a balance— you need to balance both technical depth and accessibility to a broader audience, all while making sure every chapter has a compelling narrative.

Ryan's guidance was instrumental in ensuring that each chapter struck that balance. At the start of the process, this sometimes involved not one, but two complete rewrites of the drafts. Yet by the time the final chapter was submitted, there were only two small edits, which shows how his guidance helped improve the flow and writing of the book.

Behind the scenes, Kim Kaufman, our project manager, made sure deadlines were met and provided invaluable insights on how to launch this book effectively. We also appreciated working together with the very agile Kaitlin Anthony and Katie Cosgrove.

Our gratitude extends to a group of industry experts and trusted contacts whose input enriched the final product. Special recognition is due to our "Beta Readers" whose comments helped make the end product better. They include veteran journalists like Mark Pilling and Tony Harrington as well as Andy Spinks. We are thankful to everyone who read the early drafts of this book and gave us unfiltered feedback.

The SimpliFlying team lived and breathed this book project with us. Ayushi and Shubhodeep lent their expertise, elevating the quality of our chapters, while Baiba proved once again to be an exceptional project manager, ensuring that everything happened seamlessly. A special mention goes to Ligia, our Head of Creative. You can see her work in the book's cover and graphics. Her creativity extended far beyond these pages, contributing even more visuals that will accompany us during conferences and presentations.

While the writing process was going on, Shashank made a major international move with his wife and two daughters from the mountains of Whistler, BC to the busy streets of London. He is proud of his daughters for giving him design feedback and grateful to his wife Prajakta for being with him in many nervous moments and for simply holding his hand and helping him get over the many hurdles in the way of bringing this book to life. This book would not have been possible without his family's earnest support.

For six months, Dirk dedicated every weekend and many weekdays to this book. Given his son Charlie's constant care needs, his wife Amanda and older son Ben often stepped in to help during the writing and interview sessions. He's grateful to their support, which helped get this project over the line. Looking ahead, Ben's keen interest in aviation as he plans his post-school career path is evident. We hope this book will illuminate a path towards a greener future for air travel, making it a valuable reference for those aspiring to contribute to a more sustainable world.

In closing, we want to express gratitude to every individual and organisation mentioned here. They brought *Sustainability in the Air* to life, and their support and expertise have been invaluable.

DOWNLOAD BONUS CHAPTER

Scan this QR code with the camera app on your mobile phone.

CONNECT WITH THE AUTHORS

Scan these QR codes with the camera app on your phone.

Connect directly with Shashank Nigam on LinkedIn.

Connect directly with Dirk Singer on LinkedIn.

Printed in Great Britain
by Amazon

30309435R00155